Mad, Bad or Sad?

Mad, Bad or Sad?

A Christian Approach to Antisocial Behaviour and Mental Disorder

Edited by
M Dominic Beer and
Nigel D Pocock

MAD, BAD OR SAD?
A Christian Approach to Antisocial Behaviour and Mental Disorder

Published by Christian Medical Fellowship,
6 Marshalsea Road, London SE1 1HL
www.cmf.org.uk

British Library Cataloguing-in-Publication data for this book are
available from the British Library.

Cover design by S2 Design & Advertising

ISBNs:
0 906747 35 X
978 0 906747 35 3

Originally typeset by Dr R C J Carling

Reprinted 2010 by Partridge & Print

Contents

Foreword

Andrew C P Sims

Some psychiatrists may find 'Mad, Bad or Sad?' surprising, even disturbing because of its juxtaposition of conventional 21st century British psychiatry with orthodox Christian belief in Jesus Christ, crucified, risen and active now in this complex, mad and bad world.

The authors have illuminated their practice as psychiatrists from their belief in Jesus Christ as a living and personal God, and in the Bible as a guide for daily living. They write from their experience with the mentally ill and personality disordered, disturbed adolescents and children, those addicted to alcohol and other substances and with forensic psychiatric patients.

Difficult dilemmas are met head on: how is a person at the same time both responsible for their drinking behaviour and addicted to the extent that they no longer have control? How can these two realms, the psychiatric and the Christian, when combined, lead to a helpful approach to treatment?

Please read and find out.

Andrew Sims is Emeritus Professor of Psychiatry in the University of Leeds and Past-President of The Royal College of Psychiatrists

Preface

M Dominic Beer and Nigel D Pocock

In general, the values that underpin the mental health professional's role are ones shared wholeheartedly by Christians. Care of, and respect for, individuals are fundamental Christian values. In psychiatry, most patients are given appropriate interventions without others disputing their deserving treatment. However, in a minority of cases, psychiatrists treat people who have done 'antisocial things' such as criminal acts, acts of violence, stalking, etc. The book mainly addresses the 'mad/bad' issue. However, some of these patients may be depressed, hence the 'sad' of the title.

Various trends in the secular world mean that Christian psychiatrists may face ethical dilemmas in relation to some of these patients. The increasing secularisation of society has led to less emphasis on concepts such as evil, free will and individual responsibility. In addition, the increasing pressure on professionals to predict and control those prone to violence has altered the balance between providing treatment and reducing the risk to society. These trends mean that on occasion there may be conflicts between the role expected of psychiatrists and the values that arise from their Christian faith.

This book provides a forum for Christian psychiatrists to describe some of these issues and discuss how they address/resolve them, though it is recognised that dilemmas of equal magnitude are faced by professionals in all of the caring professions. We hope that those interested in the interface between mental illness and criminal behaviour will be interested in the experiences and views detailed here and that the book will stimulate discussion, particularly among psychiatrists, other medical colleagues, psychiatric nurses, social workers, clinical psychologists, occupational therapists, probation officers, clergy, lawyers and patients. Although the authors write from a Christian perspective, the experience and expertise of the authors make the book relevant to all those interested in the subject matter.

This book has only been published with the help of others to whom the Editors are very grateful. Looking at the issue of antisocial behaviour from a Christian viewpoint was the idea of Dr John Vile, a Christian psychiatric colleague of MDB. The editors and John, with the help of the Christian Medical Fellowship, then organised a conference on this theme. Thanks are due to the speakers and contributors at that conference, who then encouraged the editors in the planning and writing of this book. We are most grateful to the chapter authors for their hard work and willingness to address the issues which the editors requested.

The staff of the Christian Medical Fellowship have been a source of much support and enthusiasm, especially Dr Peter Saunders, Dr Clare Cooper, Dr Rachael Pickering and also the members of the Publications Committee, chaired by Dr Allister Vale. Thanks are due to Dr Kathy Aitchison and Mr James Myers for their helpful comments on chapter five and to Ms Jayne Draddy for her assistance with typing. Dr Bob Carling as Production Editor and Dr Rachael Pickering as Copy Editor have helped greatly in getting the manuscript ready for publication.

Lastly, we thank our wives, Naomi Beer and Corinne Pocock, for their considerable encouragement throughout the writing of the book.

Abbreviations

Old Testament

Genesis	Gn	Song of Solomon	Song
Exodus	Ex	Isaiah	Is
Leviticus	Lv	Jeremiah	Je
Numbers	Nu	Lamentations	La
Deuteronomy	Dt	Ezekiel	Ezk
Joshua	Jos	Daniel	Dn
Judges	Jdg	Hosea	Ho
Ruth	Ru	Joel	Joel
1&2 Samuel	1&2 Sa	Amos	Am
1&2 Kings	1&2 Ki	Obadiah	Ob
1&2 Chronicles	1&2 Ch	Jonah	Jon
Ezra	Ezr	Micah	Mi
Nehemiah	Ne	Nahum	Na
Esther	Est	Habakkuk	Hab
Job	Jb	Zephaniah	Zp
Psalms	Ps	Haggai	Hg
Proverbs	Pr	Zechariah	Zc
Ecclesiastes	Ec	Malachi	Mal

New Testament

Matthew	Mt	1&2 Thessalonians	1&2 Thes
Mark	Mk	1&2 Timothy	1&2 Tim
Luke	Lk	Titus	Tit
John	Jn	Philemon	Phm
Acts	Acts	Hebrews	Heb
Romans	Rom	James	Jas
1&2 Corinthians	1&2 Cor	1&2 Peter	1&2 Pet
Galatians	Gal	1,2&3 John	1,2&3 Jn
Ephesians	Eph	Jude	Jude
Philippians	Phil	Revelation	Rev
Colossians	Col		

Contributors

M Dominic Beer MA MD FRCPsych
Consultant Psychiatrist in Challenging Behaviour and Intensive Care Psychiatry (Oxleas NHS Trust), Dartford, Kent, UK; Honorary Senior Lecturer, Division of Psychological Medicine, University of London Institute of Psychiatry, London, UK

Christopher C H Cook BSc MA MD MRCPsych
Professorial Research Fellow, Department of Theology and Religion, University of Durham, UK; formerly Professor of the Psychiatry of Alcohol Misuse, Kent Institute of Medicine & Health Sciences, University of Kent at Canterbury, UK

Elizabeth A Guinness MD MRCPsych Accredited in Child Psychiatry
Consultant Child and Adolescent Psychiatrist, East Surrey NHS Trust, UK; formerly Consultant in Third World Adult Psychiatry, Swaziland

Roger C S Moss MRCPsych DPM
Retired Consultant Psychiatrist, Devon, UK

Janet M Parrott BSc(Hons) FRCPsych Dip Crim
Consultant Forensic Psychiatrist and Clinical Director, Bracton Centre (Oxleas NHS Trust), Dartford, Kent, UK

Nigel D Pocock BA(Hons) MPhil
Social Psychologist and Theologian, Lecturer in Counselling Psychology, South London Christian College, Camberwell, London, UK

Andrew C P Sims MA MD FRCPsych FRCPE
Emeritus Professor of Psychiatry, University of Leeds, UK; Past-President of The Royal College of Psychiatrists

I

What is mental disorder?

Andrew C P Sims

This chapter describes mental disorders in the context of the mad/bad debate.

What does the Bible say about mental disorder?

How do we define mental disorder?

Is mental disorder a mental illness?

What is mental illness?

What are the main kinds of mental disorder?

Why do Christians become mentally ill?

Professor Sims examines the nature of depression, schizophrenia and gives an introduction to personality disorder.

Introduction

There can often be a similarity – a cautious optimism – in the way in which psychiatrists regard the mentally ill and the way in which Christians approach those who have done something very wrong. A psychiatrist hopes, usually with some justification, that they will be able to treat and ameliorate the symptoms and the subjective state of those who suffer from a psychiatric disorder. A Christian knows that salvation is offered to those who have done wrong, through grace, and that assurance of salvation can result in change of behaviour now, as well as offering hope for the future. This is a significant background to the so-called 'mad or bad?' debate, although the grounds for optimism are different between the two groups.

In a sense the realisation that there was a debate, that madness and badness are essentially different, was really the progenitor both of psychiatry as a medical specialty and mental disorder as a category of all illness. There are still parts of the world that have not entered into this debate – where the severely mentally ill will often be found in prison with mentally healthy criminals there also.

Looking after the insane, poor and deprived – in fact all those incapable of looking after themselves – was seen as very much a Christian responsibility by the medieval church. Thus Bethlem Hospital, 'Bedlam', was founded in 1247 as a monastery, and started to receive 'lunatics' in 1377. 'Management' at that time implied methods of restraint – manacles, chains, locks and keys and stocks.[1]

With the establishment of a monolithic, absolute Church at the time of the Counter Reformation, mental illness became bracketed with sin and possession by the devil or demons, and therefore to be managed with punishment and/or exorcism. This over-simplification of a complex problem was resisted by Juan Luis Vives who (like Galileo) was both a convinced believer and a rational thinker. Vives was concerned for the health of the human mind and believed that people could be driven insane by laughing at them and amusing oneself at their misfortune. In contradistinction to the Church in which he lived and worked, he clearly separated mental illness from evil and the 'mad or bad' distinction lives from that time forward. As the machinery of the Church for identifying heresy became more sophisticated, so the risk of all those with eccentric manners of life, including the mentally ill, became greater.

After the Reformation there were twin strands in Protestant theology and practice. On the one hand was the decision of Thomas Guy, a Baptist publisher, to develop his hospital along Christian principles, from its beginning in 1726, to establish a 'lunatic house', and the foundation of the Retreat at York at the end of the 18th Century by Quakers because of abuses at the County Lunatic Asylum. On the other hand, Protestants also burned many witches, probably including many elderly women with mental illnesses such as paranoid psychoses.[2]

Dualism still pervades the thinking of many doctors and patients. There is little difficulty in construing physical symptoms as evidence of disease, but there is much more difficulty in attributing psychological symptoms to mental illness. Thus the 'Cartesian dilemma' is also one of the roots of our current concepts of 'madness and badness'.

What does the Bible have to say about mental disorder?

Badness, evil and unrighteousness score high for mention in the Bible with a very large number of references. In contrast the Bible says virtually nothing about mental disorder. The words 'mad', 'madman' and 'madness' are used in the Old Testament on 22 occasions, and in the New Testament eight times. It is usually synonymous with pretending to be feeble, erring, foolish and also furious raving madness, 'want of thought' (*anoia*), and 'wrong mindedness' (*paraphronia*). As examples, David feigned insanity (1 Sa 21:13). When Jesus says 'I am the good shepherd', the Jews said 'he is...raving mad' (Jn 10:14,20). When Paul is on trial before Festus, he is told: 'You are out of your mind, Paul!', to which he responds 'I am not insane, most excellent Festus' (Acts 26:24,25), and then argues his case.

None of these or other quotations from the Bible says anything about mental illness as we now recognise it. Nor does Legion, whose demons entered into pigs in the story in the gospels (Lk 8:26–39), demonstrate anything like the phenomenology of modern-day schizophrenia.

However there are two very useful conclusions from the consideration of mental disorder and its treatment *in the light of the Bible*:

1. *The principle of inasmuch*: 'Inasmuch as ye have done it unto one of the least of these, ye have done it unto me' (Mt 25:40, KJV). Care for the poor – those locked up, either physically or metaphorically, the deprived, the bereaved and the sick – is the heart of gospel teaching. Christian individuals, institutions and psychiatrists share common goals. The Magnificat teaches us that the gospel is first and foremost for the poor and deprived.

2. Illuminating our psychiatric *practice in the light of the Bible* is valuable. Dominian[3] has given us helpful insights through looking at the biblical account of the life of Jesus Christ through the eyes of a psychiatrist – for example, how the secure and successful relationship developed in Jesus' childhood with both of his parents led to human maturity in his adult work with difficult people and people with difficulties.

Mental illness in the Bible: an example

The Bible does not purport to be a textbook of psychiatry and never attempts to present symptoms for ease of psychiatric diagnosis! However, many commentators have tried to give such a diagnosis in order to explain the behaviour and state of mind of biblical characters. It is frequently stated, for example, that King Saul suffered from mental illness. Let us now examine this assertion in more detail.

Was Saul mentally ill at any time during his comparatively long life (he reigned from the age of 30 for 42 years)? If so, what was the diagnosis and how did this interact with his life story?

There is a considerable amount written about Saul in the Old Testament books of 1 & 2 Samuel and 1 Chronicles; he is mentioned in about 40 chapters and his state of mind, physique and behaviour are frequently described. Despite this relative richness of material, a cautious psychiatrist would consider that there is insufficient evidence and would be reluctant to make a diagnosis – there are some hints but these are far from conclusive.

We read that Saul was a young man without equal in Israel, literally head and shoulders above his fellow soldiers. Before his anointing as King, he was sensitive to the proprieties in being concerned about not having a gift to bring to the prophet, and to the anxieties of others in realising that his father would worry if he was away from home for too long. He was aware of his humble origins and he was initially quite shy about his newly exalted situation.

Several times we read that God changed Saul's heart and the Spirit of God came upon him in power. As a result of this he joined in uninhibited dancing and in prophesying. When provoked by his enemies, 'the Spirit of God came upon him in power and he burned with anger'. His anger was followed by effective and, by contemporary standards, appropriate military action. He could be magnanimous towards his detractors, but also he could be very foolish and he made several rash promises that subsequently he must have much regretted.

Acquisition of power turned his head, and, not satisfied with the role of absolute monarch, he aspired to the equally powerful position of priest as well. This was utterly forbidden to him in Jewish law. In response to this, Samuel the prophet had to say, 'You acted foolishly … your kingdom will not endure'. From this point onwards, no longer a young man, his life course and demeanour progressively deteriorates – everything goes wrong. He no longer obeys Samuel, he seeks to kill David who has been chosen to be his successor and he rebels against God. Every now and then there are chinks of insight and he admits to his unrighteousness, saying, 'I have sinned'. Even his son Jonathan is conscious of his father's foolish, unjust and homicidal behaviour.

Saul also shows extremes of mood. Both elation and despondency are described as the Spirit of God coming upon him – 'The Spirit of God came upon him and he started prophesying' on at least two occasions. 'An evil spirit from the Lord came upon Saul and he tried to pin David to the wall with his spear.' With one sort of spirit he was elated and disinhibited; with the other sort, he was miserable, despondent, filled with jealousy and homicidal rage. On one such occasion, he killed Ahimelech and all his family. Early on, the episodes of low mood could be relieved by music, especially David playing the harp. His murderous intentions were not just impulsive but also premeditated – he sent men to watch David's house and kill him the next day. Saul was intensely afraid of David because he knew him to be 'more righteous than I...You have treated me well but I have treated you badly'. Saul's life ends in him killing himself, but it is an heroic and altruistic suicide; he falls on his sword when he knows that the battle is lost.

Is this an account of mental illness? Well, it could be but it does not have to be. As a psychiatrist, I cannot make an unequivocal diagnosis with the given information. It may be that he suffered from what is now called bipolar affective disorder or, previously, manic-depressive psychosis, but this is not certain. There is evidence of mood swings, from ecstatic elation with disinhibited behaviour and excited utterings, to profound depression with feelings of jealousy, envy and rage, and ultimately suicide: all potential indicators of such a condition but by no means absolute proof. However, the elation had more of spiritual enlightenment than manic excitement, the despondency was a realistic reaction to his state and his suicide was by no means typical of pathological dejection. All in all, the evidence is not convincing.

A cautious diagnostician would concur with bipolar disorder as a possibility. Even if Saul did suffer from this condition it does not appear to have much explanatory value concerning the course of his life – for example, it does not explain his offering sacrifices or attempting to murder David. Looking for the signs of mental illness does little to help us understand Saul. That is not why we were given the biblical account and the Bible does not give us that sort of information. Although there is little value in looking for psychiatric signs and symptoms in the Bible, assessing stories and individual characters from the viewpoint of a psychiatrist, such as having some understanding of family dynamics, can give valuable and fresh insights. That is the position of Dominian in the book recommended below.

What is mental disorder?

Mental disorder is not unitary, either in causation, manifestation, theoretical formulation or in style of management. Thus the *cause* of a dementing illness such as Alzheimer's disease is clearly a disease of the brain that produces abnormalities readily apparent down the microscope, whereas the cause of agoraphobia, fear of going into a crowded place, is a developmental and environmental disorder with little to do with the structure of the brain. The *manifestations* of mental illnesses, symptoms, vary from delusions and hallucinations of psychotic disorder to disturbance of behaviour that is inappropriate in achieving that person's own individual goals, characteristic of neurotic disorders. A *theoretical formulation* in terms of the psychodynamics of the family and the way this individual's early upbringing infringed upon his subsequent development is clearly very different from a formulation based upon abnormalities in the brain cells of people suffering from a similar condition, such as 'depression'. The *style of management* may vary, from physical treatments such as the use of psychotropic drugs or electroconvulsive therapy, to cognitive behavioural therapy or psychoanalysis. It is also important to think about the social determinants of mental illness and the scope they give for effective treatment. Conceptualising the problem of the individual patient cannot be unitary; biological, psychological, social and spiritual aspects must always be considered.

Table 1.1 shows the range of mental disorders as described in the *ICD-10 Classification of Mental and Behavioural Disorders*.[4] Individual mental disorders may be subsumed under generic categories. The mad/bad debate is relevant to a different extent for each of these separate categories. Thus with *organic mental disorders*, where mental illness results from localised brain disease or brain disturbance resulting from generalised illness, it is unlikely that anyone will impute disturbed behaviour to causes other than the brain disorder itself. *Psychoactive substance use*, which includes addiction and misuse of alcohol and other drugs, gives rise to considerable debate as to whether it is the individual's 'fault', or whether it is an illness, or the person has become an accidental victim of his social circumstances. Thus the mad/bad debate is a significant factor with this diagnostic category. *Schizophrenia* is now almost universally regarded as a brain disease for which there is increasing

Table 1.1   Mental disorders in *ICD-10* (see ref. 4) and the 'mad/bad' debate

Organic mental disorders	–
Psychoactive substance use	++
Schizophrenia	+
Mood (affective) disorders	+
Neurotic and related disorders	+
Personality disorder and behaviour	+++
Mental retardation	–
Disorders of psychological development	–
Disorders of childhood & adolescence	+

– no association between illness and antisocial behaviour
+ some association between illness and antisocial behaviour
++ considerable association between illness and antisocial behaviour
+++ great association between illness and antisocial behaviour

evidence of specific disorganised brain physiology. However when a person suffering from schizophrenia acts in an inappropriate or unacceptable way, this may occur because of their underlying schizophrenic symptoms or, alternatively, from that part of the person that has not been affected by the condition. Similarly, with *mood or affective disorders* unacceptable behaviour may result from the underlying disturbed mood state or from parts of the person not affected by their illness. In *neurotic disorders* there is always an inappropriate response to what the individual conceives as stress, either internal or external. Again, selfish or even criminal acts may either result from the underlying condition or from the person unaffected by a mental disorder.

It is with discussion of *personality disorder* in psychiatry that there is the greatest scope for debate on whether the individual's activity and demeanour is a result of mental illness or intrinsic badness. Personality disorder is seen as resulting from the constitution or permanent characteristics of the individual, rather than a transient or even long lasting state of disease. *Mental retardation* (learning disability) is an intellectual impairment or lack of capacity that has occurred at or before birth or very early in childhood. Antisocial or criminal activity may occur as a result of impaired intellect or because of the person's intrinsic response unaffected by their impaired intellect. *Disorders of psychological development,* such as specific reading disorder or autism, have no real association with the mad/bad debate. In *child psychiatry* disturbance in behaviour and antisocial acts may arise as a result of the psychiatric condition or independent of it.

An example of a criminal act occurring as a direct result of mental illness would be the man who was convicted of the manslaughter of his son by placing the boy on the handlebars of his bicycle and cycling into the harbour. It later transpired that the man had been severely depressed at the time and the only person he cared for in the world was his son. He had decided to kill himself and he wanted to save his son from a long and miserable life. His plans went awry when he was pulled alive out of the harbour whilst his son had drowned. An example of an instance where criminal behaviour did not arise from the individual's mental illness is the case of a woman who was so severely phobic that she was unable to go out of her house although she felt quite comfortable when on her own at home. She had claimed a financial allowance for her partner to be off work and look after her full time, whereas at that time he was not even living with her. These examples might seem simple and straightforward but obviously discrimination may be highly complex. However, it is important not to impute badness to those who are involuntarily expressing their mental illness.

Is mental disorder illness?

This question craves definitions of 'mental disorder' and 'illness'. As Peter Sedgwick[5] has put it: 'All departments of nature below the level of mankind are exempt both from disease and from treatment – until man intervenes with his own human classifications of disease and treatment. The blight that strikes at corn or at potatoes is a *human invention,* for if man wished to cultivate parasites (rather than potatoes or corn) there would be no "blight", but simply the necessary foddering of the parasite-crop'. Thus because we want to grow potatoes we categorise potato blight as a 'disease of potatoes'. Ultimately disease or illness is a social construct.

In trying to decide what is and what is not mental illness it is useful to consider different dimensions, for example, contrasting the mentally ill with the mentally healthy. An entirely separate and independent dimension is good/bad or right/wrong. That these variables are independent of each other is obvious but it does need stating. Mentally ill people may be good or bad, right or wrong, and so may healthy people be. However, there may be an association with some of the characteristics that we regard as being bad or wrong with certain specific mental illnesses, for example, unpredictableness, aggressiveness, callousness and selfishness – the first three more often with psychotic disorders, and the last with neurotic disorder. Quite often people with psychiatric illness may be unaware of the effects of their behaviour upon other people's mental state and physical comfort, for example the severely depressed elderly woman who said to her doctor in front of her caring daughter, 'everybody hates me, and I might as well be dead'. Sometimes because of their mental illness they may be unable to prevent themselves from doing what they know to be wrong, for example a patient with schizophrenia who believed himself compelled to shout obscenities. On rare occasions, because of a mental illness, an individual may be unable to distinguish between right and wrong as in the McNaughton defence for murder: 'To establish a defence on the ground of insanity, it must be clearly proved that at the time of the committing of the act the accused party was labouring under such defect of reason, from disease of the mind, as not to know the nature and quality of the act he was doing, or, if he did know it, that he did not know he was doing what was wrong'.[6]

For physical illnesses, diagnosis is generally made by applying a pathological model. Thus for fatal lobar pneumonia the gross naked eye changes of consolidation of a lobe of the lung would be found, the characteristic changes would be revealed microscopically and the causative organism might be cultured. In general, the pathological model cannot be applied in psychiatry except for organic mental disorders. The physical substrate explains nowhere near the whole picture.

The World Health Organization definition of health in 1946 stated: 'Health is a state of complete physical, mental and social well-being and not merely the absence of disease or infirmity'.[7] In practice the doctor's job is to treat individual suffering and therefore most doctors use the word *disorder* or *illness* to apply to conditions for which we have available techniques for treatment or amelioration.

Another pitfall is to distinguish mental disorder from physical illness as if the two were opposed and separate. In practice every severe 'physical' illness will have psychological consequences such as pain or loss of energy or lowering of mood, and severe psychiatric disorder presents with physical symptoms, such as loss of appetite and weight and sleep disorder, as in major depressive illness. Kendell has made the point: 'Not only is the distinction between mental and physical illness ill-founded and incompatible with contemporary understanding of disease, it is also damaging to the long-term interests of patients themselves'.[8]

What is depression?

The umbrella term 'depression' contains a wide range of different conditions with different causes. Manic depressive or bipolar affective disorder is characterised by profound swings of mood from severe, perhaps suicidal, depression to elation and over-activity which is equally pathological. In unipolar affective disorder severe episodes of depression occur without ever showing the contrasted, manic mood. Depression may occur as an apparent response to genetic or biochemical causes from inside the person or it may be reactive to external stressors such as domestic or work difficulties. Depression may be mild, in which the quality of life is impaired but the person is able to remain working and carrying out their normal activities, or severe, in which the person may be completely disabled by their illness and unable to function adequately in any of their usual situations. One can use different models to conceptualise the cause, nature and outcome of depression: biological, social, epidemiological, phenomenological, cognitive, psychodynamic models, and so on. These demonstrate the huge diversity that lies within the simple word 'depression'.

A characteristic constellation of symptoms occurs with depressed mood, loss of interest and enjoyment, and decreased energy resulting in an increase of fatigability and decreased activity. There also tends to be an impairment of concentration and attention, lowered self esteem and self confidence, ideas of guilt and unworthiness, and a bleak and pessimistic view of the future. Ideas or acts of self harm or suicide may occur. There is virtually always disturbance of sleep and there may be loss of appetite with consequent loss of weight. A depressed person is unlikely to carry out some antisocial acts simply because of the lack of energy and initiative that accompanies the condition. However, depressive mood may of itself lead to certain types of crime, for example, infanticide in the mother severely depressed after childbirth. Clearly, in such a case demonstration of the presence of a psychiatric illness would demand that the condition be treated and mitigate the severity of the sentence.

What is schizophrenia?

Schizophrenia is a severe, debilitating and often chronic illness in which sufferers appear to lose touch with reality. Conventionally, the characteristic symptoms are described as *positive* or *negative*. Positive symptoms include *delusions* in which there are false beliefs, *hallucinations* – false perceptions of which auditory hallucinations of voices are especially frequent, and *disorder of the thinking process*. These symptoms do not occur in all people with schizophrenia and those who show these symptoms are not necessarily suffering from schizophrenia. However, they are the symptoms from which the diagnosis of schizophrenia is most often made.

The negative symptoms all imply a loss of mental function. They include loss of energy for carrying out normal activities, loss of the usual, expected feelings in relationships or for social situations, loss of social skills, a lack of communication and diminution of physical drives, including sexual activity. These negative symptoms tend to occur later in the course of the illness and over the long term tend to cause more disability and lack of social adaptation than the more prominent, positive symptoms, which generally respond better and more quickly to treatment.

There is still much to be learned about the causes of schizophrenia. There appears to be a genetic predisposition in some sufferers from the condition, but 60% have no family history and the precise genetic mechanism is not known. There appears to be some association between developing the illness and a very early disturbance of brain function or structure. There is an increased rate for schizophrenia in those suffering from obstetric difficulties at the time of their birth; there is also evidence for some people to develop the condition following maternal viral infection in early mid-pregnancy, but this at most would only account for about three percent of cases. There has been some evidence for emotional and environmental factors being precipitating causes but this would only be causative if other, predisposing causes are present. Sometimes the onset of the condition has been associated with, and follows taking, illicit drugs such as cannabis or heroin. In discussing cause of schizophrenia it is particularly important to make a distinction between predisposing, precipitating and perpetuating factors.

The prevalence of schizophrenia, where it has been studied world wide, is remarkably constant. The life-long risk of developing schizophrenia is just under one in 100. There are about 250,000 cases in the United Kingdom at any time; onset is usually between the ages of 15 and 30 in men and 25 to 45 in women. About one-third of homeless people will be suffering from schizophrenia; the condition is also over-represented among those who have never married, who are separated or divorced.

The outcome in schizophrenia is very variable but recovery or improvement is more likely if appropriate treatment is given at an early stage after symptoms first manifest. There is a considerably increased risk for suicide amongst sufferers from schizophrenia and this risk demands regular monitoring of the patient's mental state. The long-term deterioration of mental function that may accompany this illness tends eventually to plateau, perhaps with a considerable degree of disability. In almost all cases treatment will combine pharmacological and psychosocial aspects with the use of psychotropic drugs such as chlorpromazine, and careful attention to the needs of the whole person within his or her family environment.

What is personality disorder?

The answer to this question is the nub of the whole mad/bad debate. There are various dilemmas that make this topic a conceptual minefield:

- Personality has an enormous effect upon the person's whole life.
- Measuring and assessing personality is not precise – on the whole the more scientific and statistically reliable the measurement the less useful it is.
- That part of the personality that is not manifest is probably much more important than what is – rather like an iceberg.

The term personality disorder is used with two rather different meanings:

1. To describe the situation when problems for mental health or behaviour arise directly from abnormality of the personality.
2. Sometimes, in a medico-legal situation it has had the more restricted meaning of simply referring to antisocial aspects of behaviour arising from what was previously called psychopathic personality.

The former meaning is recommended for general use as it is less restrictive and pejorative and fits better with the rest of psychological and psychiatric terminology.[9]

To understand the term 'personality disorder' one needs to have a concept of the meaning of personality in a mental health context. Subjectively, it is the unique quality of an individual in terms of his feelings and personal goals. Objectively, personality describes the characteristic behaviour of an individual, his persistent actions and patterns. Personality includes an individual's emotional state and their aims and goals, but it excludes intelligence and physical constitution. It is always manifested in social relationships.

Abnormal personality should imply the statistical use of the word 'normal', ie the individual has significantly more or less of some particular characteristic than other people who would be regarded as having a normal amount of it. Thus if 'the milk of human kindness' could be made into a measurable personality characteristic, both Hitler and St Francis would be abnormal in personality, the former having considerable deficiency in volume of this characteristic and the latter having a statistically significant excess. Abnormal personality then is a variation upon an accepted yet broadly conceived range of average personality.

Certain aspects of personality are considered to be clinically important. These personality *types* constitute the different personality disorders listed in psychiatric classifications, for example, *ICD-10*.[4] Some of these specific personality disorders listed are *anxious*, *paranoid* and *obsessional* personality disorder. Thus, if an individual has anxious or obsessional characteristics to an abnormal extent he or she may be considered to have abnormal personality of that type. If this characteristic causes suffering either to the patient or to other people then personality disorder is considered to be present. Types of personality disorder described in *ICD-10* are listed in Table 1.2.

The social environment is all important. A person who is considered to be a psychopath in one society may be regarded as a charismatic leader in another. A social misfit in one type of environment may prove to be a great success when social conditions have changed. It is very important to realise that not all personality disorder is associated with an increased rate of criminal behaviour. In fact a person suffering from anankastic or obsessional personality disorder has a considerably decreased likelihood of involvement in illegal behaviour. The whole field of personality disorder is under the public spotlight at present and the interested reader is directed to Livesley.[10]

Table 1.2 Specific personality disorders in *ICD-10* (see ref. 4)

F60.0	Paranoid personality disorder
F60.1	Schizoid personality disorder
F60.2	Dissocial personality disorder
F60.3	Emotionally unstable personality disorder
F60.30	Impulsive type
F60.31	Borderline type
F60.4	Histrionic personality disorder
F60.5	Anankastic personality disorder
F60.6	Anxious (avoidant) personality disorder
F60.7	Dependent personality disorder

Why do Christians become mentally ill?

Christians share their common humanity with the rest of the population of the world. They are subject to almost all the biological stresses that may result in mental disorder and most of the psychosocial and environmental stresses. For example, Alzheimer's disease has a biological cause, it is an organic mental disorder, and affects individuals predisposed irrespective of their beliefs or behaviours. Post-traumatic stress disorder occurs as a response to an extremely stressful event or situation of an exceptionally threatening or catastrophic nature capable of causing distress in almost anyone, such as involvement in a natural or man-made disaster, war, witnessing the violent death of others or being a victim of torture, terrorism or rape. No one is automatically immune from such disasters and anyone may respond with severe psychological symptoms, in the same way that anyone may experience broken ribs when their chest is compressed by a heavy weight.

The mentally ill person is a victim, a patient, a sufferer. The gist of biblical teaching is not that we will be exempt from the problems and vicissitudes of life but rather that we have resources to transform these problems. A Christian patient of mine experienced several episodes of severe depressive illness requiring inpatient admission and electroconvulsive therapy (ECT) for treatment. She recovered fully and has remained well for many years. She considered that depression had been allowed to affect her by God and because of her experiences she has had an increased usefulness to the Church.

There is no doubt that at times the harsh and extreme religious and behavioural demands of certain sects and churches have been causative factors in the development of mental illness, especially depression. An emphasis on guilt and fault finding has had a harmful effect on mental health, and exclusion from a church fellowship, for what the leaders have seen as sinfulness but may be no more than lack of compliance with that group's norms, may be devastating.

The practising Christian has great resources that are beneficial in dealing with mental illness. These are numerous but the most significant are the value and reassurance of faith in Christ and the strength and support that come from fellowship in the Church. Larson and co-workers[11] have accumulated evidence to show that church attendance and religious belief is associated with better outcome following clinically established mental illness.

2

Childhood influences on antisocial behaviour

Elizabeth A Guinness

The premise of the 'mad/bad' debate in this chapter states that moral responsibility does not lie so much with the individual as with the social group.

To what extent do the social influences on individuals affect their future behaviour?

Is moral responsibility socially determined as well as an individual phenomenon?

What are the important childhood influences on future adult behaviour?

What are important factors which may hinder moral responsibility?

How do social and family influences interact in the formation of personality?

Introduction

The 'mad or bad' debate essentially questions whether moral responsibility is a useful concept. The deliberately imprecise terms 'mad' or 'bad' are sometimes used to challenge a judgmental attitude, or as an ironic comment on the human capacity for moral choices. If a person is so poorly endowed genetically, or has had such a deprived or abused childhood that they suffer mental disorder, can they be held responsible for their actions? What part is played by the culture and beliefs of society in socialising its members and upholding what is 'good'? Other chapters in this book will address the more serious aspects of this, where 'badness' must be defined as criminal behaviour and 'madness' as serious mental illness, such as psychosis, leading to diminished responsibility in law. This chapter however, starts where it all begins – in childhood, where the human personality is shaped. It offers a brief overview, according to research and practice, of child development and psychiatry so as to inform the debate.

'Mad' or 'bad' for this purpose needs a broader, more subtle definition denoting what hinders a person from being 'good'. That curious legal concept of 'how the average man in the street would see it' comes in useful here. Thus 'badness' is defined as infringement of the social code. 'Madness' is defined as a state of mind or behaviour requiring help or treatment, and for which allowances should be made.

This chapter is presented in three parts. First, it examines how the human and social environment of childhood determines the way in which the genetic phenotype is developed to form the adult personality. The phenotype is the expression in the living person of the genetic blueprint (the genotype). Genetic research has mapped out not only the strong genetic component of many mental disorders but also demonstrated genetic influences across the whole range of human behaviour.[1] Indeed, it should not surprise us to find that the way the brain works is strongly influenced by the genes. But does it follow that we are victims of our genes, predetermined in terms of moral responsibility, will power or life choices? These are key issues for the mad/bad debate.

Severe mental disorder only appears when the adverse genes are fully expressed in the phenotype. Many other genes have a modifying influence so that more often a genetic vulnerability results. Thus a broad spectrum of milder traits is found in other family members, for instance in families having autism, mood disorder or Attention Deficit with Hyperactivity Disorder (ADHD). In childhood it is possible to see these genetic traits of mental function in their simplest form before adaptations and complications (acquired comorbidity) obscure them. Furthermore there is complex interplay between nature and nurture. Genetic vulnerability may be maximised or minimised by the psychosocial environment.

The second part of the chapter describes imprinting on the infant brain. Although the potential for brain development is genetic, the actual 'wiring up' in neuronal pathways depends upon the appropriate stimuli being received from the five senses during critical periods in the first years of life. The nurturing environment, particularly the mother–infant relationship, is crucial. Many aspects of dysfunctional personality development leading to 'bad' behaviour can be traced back to faulty imprinting due to adverse early family life.

The third part of the chapter explores how society operates to safeguard family life. We need a theoretical framework to focus this discussion. Social conventions, cultural customs, belief systems, even 'political correctness' are not readily definable entities. As the saying goes: 'Morality wherever met is merely local etiquette'. A scientific approach to human social relationships is needed.

The school of thought that has contributed most to the understanding of family dysfunction, and led to the development of family therapy, is Systems Theory.[2] This states that any group of people who live or work together, be it a family, a school or a workplace, will create a set of dynamics and beliefs that influence how its members think, feel and behave. A natural hierarchy emerges, although the power base, or dominance, may not be that of the ostensible leadership. Unwritten rules and expectations become apparent. Members are largely unaware of the beliefs of the system. However, they experience pressure to conform to what that particular system requires. In a dysfunctional system the members will suffer symptoms. Systems Theory also holds that there will be groups within groups. The subsystems which are chiefly concerned in rearing children are families and schools. These belong to neighbourhood communities which in turn are part of national society. The wider system or 'suprasystem' profoundly influences how the subsystems function. How much does the power of the family system operate to structure and support individual (genetic) weakness and so reinforce self control? The mad/bad debate will be carried forward by identifying the appropriate locus of moral responsibility. Does it lie most meaningfully with the individual or the group?

Disentangling nature and nurture

Earlier research techniques for identifying vulnerability and protective factors that predicted adult mental health involved prospective follow through studies. Cohorts of children were reassessed at intervals over 20 years. Classic examples include West and Farrington's (1973) Study on the Origins of Delinquency[3] and the Newcastle Thousand Family Study on the Cycle of Deprivation (Miller 1988).[4] Genetic disadvantage in terms of lowish IQ, dyslexia and developmental delays, combined with harsh and inconsistent parenting in a setting of social adversity, put children at risk of delinquency in later life. Yet some children seem to survive unscathed from the most adverse environments. Protective factors include good learning ability whereby school becomes a haven. The opportunity for, or the social skills to acquire, a nurturing relationship with a different adult also reduces the risk.

More sophisticated research techniques were needed to tease out the primary genetic component from the impact of the rearing environment. Twin and adoption studies have been key tools. Some countries, such as Scandinavia, keep national registers of twins and of psychiatric disorders to facilitate such research. Twin studies involve collecting two series of twin pairs, one or both of which has the disorder. If the series of monozygotic twins (those having identical genes) shows a greater concordance with both twins having the disorder than the non-identical, dizygotic series, then there must be strong heritability. Autism has a 90% concordance rate.[5] Schizophrenia is also strongly genetic but the concordance is only 46%, thus indicating some environmental effects which precipitate the vulnerability.[1] Manic depressive disorder has 80% concordance, whereas simple depression is only 20–40% genetic. Kendler[6] showed that families in the latter group demonstrated a dimension of neuroticism or emotionality with a greater vulnerability to depression with adverse life experience.

The inheritance of these mental disorders is not by a single gene according to simple Mendelian principles – it is polygenic and complex, with many genes interacting to produce a continuum within a population sharing the same genetic pool. Some developmental disorders of childhood seem to be at the extreme end of the continuum. Intelligence is one such polygenic dimension, the extreme end of which is mental retardation (see Fig. 2.1a). ADHD is another. ADHD is now considered to be an inherited dimensional characteristic rather than a disorder.[7] Some researchers suggest that autism is the extreme deficit of a dimension of empathy. Gillberg[8] reviewed population research in Sweden on the autistic spectrum disorders, and postulated an 'empathy quotient' analogous to the intelligence quotient (see Fig. 2.1b) across the normal population. This hypothesis of various dimensions of human mental function has interesting implications for the mad/bad debate. Let the reader consider as you read this chapter where you would place yourself in five possible dimensions.

Intelligence

Intelligence is predominantly genetic. It is distributed across the population according to the bell-shaped curve of normal distribution. The extreme end of low IQ is further weighted by actual physical disorders of the brain such as birth injury, severe childhood illness or malnutrition, chromosomal abnormalities such as Down's Syndrome or rare genetic (single gene) abnormalities of metabolism (see Fig. 2.1a). Rearing environments within the normal range have little influence on IQ development (see review by Rutter[9]). However, severe disadvantage and neglect substantially impair IQ (see imprinting research review by Glaser[10]).

Nonetheless, educational attainment and learning are not simply determined by IQ – emotional and social well being are key factors. A child cannot realise their intellectual potential if he or she is emotionally disturbed or is not having their primary needs for parenting adequately met. Children who are assessed as having Special Educational Needs requiring special schooling are as likely to have emotional and behavioural problems as learning difficulties.

There were several important cohort studies on how much IQ could be increased by improving early rearing. The Headstart Program was part of the War on Poverty in New York in the 1960s (see commentary by Besharov[11] and the Milwaukee Project[12]). Intensive input was given in the preschool years, including support for the mothers in their parenting and high quality play school for the children. Although all input ceased when the children were five years old, significant benefits continued to be detected. During their school days there were fewer special educational needs, in their teens there was less delinquency, and as young adults there were better employment records. However, these were not due to increased measurable IQ. Other factors were operating.

Intelligence is only one dimension of mental function. A child with high intelligence may be considerably handicapped by autistic spectrum disorder or ADHD, whereas a child with a lowish IQ may cope quite well in life if he or she is normal in these dimensions.

Autistic spectrum disorder

Severe autism of the type classically described by Kanner[13] is rare and of stable incidence in the population around five per 10,000.[14] It is largely genetic, although birth complications, neonatal infections and various rare medical disorders can contribute (Fig. 2.1b). The actual neuropathology is little understood.[15]

Fig. 2.1a Normal distribution of intelligence

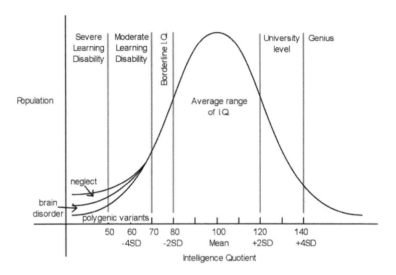

Fig. 2.1b Normal distribution of empathy showing relative prevalence of autism and Asperger syndrome

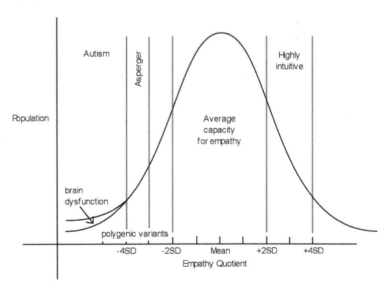

The autistic person is inaccessible to human interaction, aloof, cut off, unable to communicate emotionally, non-verbally or even through language in severe cases. Associated mental retardation in 80% of severe autistics may contribute to the lack of language. Even when speech is present it is abnormal, being concrete, literal and not used for meaningful mutual communication. Indeed autistic people cannot comprehend that fellow human beings think and feel at all. This is called lack of 'Theory of Mind'. The human social world is a frightening mystery to them.

Asperger's Syndrome is a milder version of autism. It is primarily a deficit of non-verbal communication, a lack of empathy. It can be seen in varying degrees of severity in child development practice. Normal people do not appreciate how much we all communicate non-verbally by facial expression, body language, tone of voice, innuendo and idiom. Imagine what life must be like for those unable to do this! Asperger children (and adults) cannot detect praise, disapproval or embarrassment in others. Therefore they cannot modify their behaviour to socially acceptable norms. Concepts of right and wrong in childhood are developed largely through such non-verbal communication.[16] Asperger sufferers must learn by logic rather than intuition.

In adolescence they have a bad time. The sophistication of peer group social interaction increases sharply and they begin to realise the extent of their disability. Adjusting to change and launching into adult life can be very difficult. They cannot make friends so can find no socially acceptable outlet for sexual drive. They become lonely eccentric adults. The Asperger tendency to intense obsessional interests combined with sexual frustration can potentially fuel crimes of sexual violence. However autistic disorders do not predict criminal offending in the way childhood ADHD and Conduct Disorders do. Asperger people are more liable to depression because of their disability and are at greater risk of schizophrenia.[17]

Research in recent years (reviewed by Gillberg 1992[8]) has demonstrated a strong familial loading for milder expressions of autistic-like disorder. If the extended family tree of an autistic child is mapped out, there may be only one or two members with severe Kanner autism. Several more relatives would show the milder Asperger's Syndrome and others various combinations of disorders of language, perception, attention and motor control. Rank and file members would show higher rates of mild social communication deficit than average. Hence comes the concept of an empathy dimension.

It is probably this much wider recognition of the broad spectrum of the autistic phenotype that has led to the greater incidence of autism in recent years. Gillberg[18] reckons the prevalence of the broad spectrum disorders is 40–50 per 10,000. The difficulty in estimating the prevalence is consistent with the dimensional hypothesis (Fig. 2.1a, b & c), ie where the cut-off point is. However, there is always an underlying worry that there might be a real increase and this has fuelled the controversy over the MMR vaccine.

Fig. 2.1c Normal distribution of Executive Function showing varying severity of Attention Definition Disorder

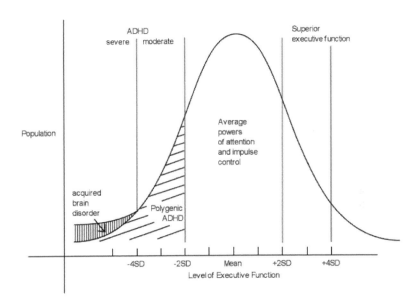

Attention deficit hyperactivity disorder

Research into attention deficit hyperactivity disorder (ADHD) suggests that it is essentially a disorder of executive function.[19] Executive function is the capacity of the mind to organise itself, utilise experience and knowledge, exercise concentration and impulse control, prioritise, plan ahead and defer gratification.

Children with ADHD show one or more of three core symptoms: hyperactivity, impulsivity and inattentiveness to varying degrees. The underlying neuropsychology of ADHD is a critically weak short-term working memory whereby the train of thought cannot be held in the forefront of the mind for long enough for executive function to operate. Deficient levels of the synaptic neurotransmitter dopamine, leading to inadequate cortical activation (underarousal), is a possible mechanism. Methylphenidate medication (Ritalin) acts by fine-tuning the dopamine levels.[20]

There are many differences in the phenotype of ADHD. The subtype with a strong impulsivity and hyperactivity component is a predictive factor for adult antisocial personality disorder.[21] The subtype with inattentiveness only is now regarded as a distinct disorder, better termed Higher Cognitive Dysfunction.[22] This does not predict criminality but rather co-morbid anxiety and depression. Intense effort is needed to focus attention, to plan and prioritise. It is essential for such people to find jobs that favour their strengths rather than taxing their weaknesses.

In other subtypes of ADHD there are various abnormalities of attention as well as attention deficit. Some show perseverative attention – they become engrossed and cannot switch channels. Others have an inability to select the channel of attention. The child responds on all channels and becomes flooded, hyper-stimulated. Such children actively seek solitude (even hiding in cupboards). They need their immediate environment to be carefully stage-managed if they are to function at all.

There is considerable overlap between the autistic spectrum disorders and ADHD. A child with both types of deficit would certainly be more vulnerable in later life.

Treatment of ADHD neatly exemplifies our definition of 'mad or bad' and the premise of the debate that moral responsibility lies with the social group rather than solely with the individual. Treatment takes three forms. First, adults, parents and teachers must understand the limitations that ADHD imposes upon the child and make allowances. ADHD children are infuriating to live with; they create chaos around themselves and repeatedly fail to meet adult expectations. To require them to do so will only result in opposition and despair. Adults must manage the children's lives for them by creating much structure, routine and predictability. Given a well-ordered home life with much training in habits, with opportunity for positive experiences and appropriate schooling, ADHD children will not become disordered and delinquent. Treatment with Ritalin facilitates this. Parent training is essential. See Figures 2.2a and 2.2b which explain how the ADHD can be either controlled or worsened according to the quality of home life and parenting. Psychological therapies for the child such as behavioural modification help.

Fig. 2.2a ADHD: Bad Outcome. The parents cannot stage-manage home life

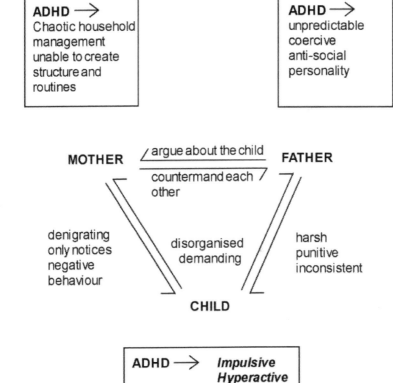

Cognitive therapy can be attempted but is disappointing. Sadly all too often the opposite type of home environment prevails because the parents also have ADHD traits. Instead of order being created around the child, family life is chaotic, parenting is harsh and inconsistent so that co-morbid behaviour problems develop. There is a well researched continuity between Oppositional Defiant Disorder in young children, Conduct Disorder in older children, teenage delinquency and adult antisocial personality disorder.[23]

Fig. 2.2b ADHD: Good Outcome. Good parenting minimises the ADHD

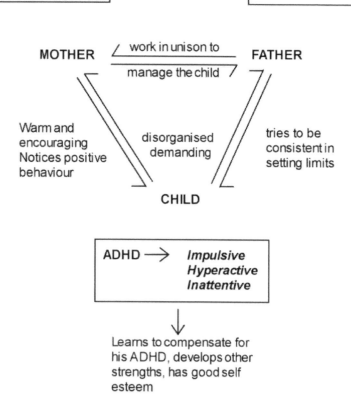

The ADHD child will be less at risk of developing Conduct Disorder if one parent (usually the mother) has a different genetic endowment without ADHD and can create order in the home.

Antecedents of antisocial personality disorder

Rutter[1] discusses how the complex interactions between genes and environment augment the risk of adult criminality in various subtle ways. Thus the parents who pass on the genes are the same adults who provide the rearing environment. Personality disordered parents will tend to create dysfunctional family systems without coherent frames of reference for the children. Furthermore antisocial adults are likely to select adverse life styles characterised by criminality, violence, the drug scene and unemployment.

Assortive mating, ie selection of a partner with a similar disposition is more likely with antisocial personalities. It compounds the genetic loading in the offspring. Indeed one way to escape the cycle of deprivation is to do the opposite and to marry a healthy normal partner.[4] Finally the child's own genetic constitution shapes the parenting received in a process of circular causality. For example the difficult, impulsive, inattentive child with ADHD is more likely to receive a punitive response than his easier sibling.

Thus, although the family environment is shared, the child induces a non-shared environment. One must always hesitate to blame parents. If they had had an easier child they might have done a better job.

Table 2.1 Findings of adoptee studies predicting risk of adult criminality (see ref. 28)

Genetic risk	Environmental risk	Risk of adult criminality
Low	Low	3%
Low	High	6%
High	Low	12%
High	High	40%

Bohman[24] concludes from adoption studies that adverse environments have only a weak effect in producing adult antisocial behaviour when there is no genetic risk. Table 2.1 also shows that the genetic risk can be substantially reduced by good rearing. Children reared apart from antisocial biological parents (adopted) were only twelve per cent as likely to become antisocial instead of 40%.

Rutter[1] also points out the genetic differences between life-course persistent antisocial behaviour in adults and delinquency that occurs only during the adolescent years. Simple juvenile delinquency has a low genetic component and is more a reflection of the values of the suprasystem, eg the ethos prevailing on a housing estate (see below). These findings are important for informing political initiatives for crime prevention. Setting limits as in 'zero tolerance' programmes and the positive alternatives provided by youth work, make good sense. However prevention of more serious persistent crime means targeting the predictive factors in childhood. ADHD is one. Dysfunctional parenting is another. Faulty imprinting is much less amenable to change after the critical period is passed. Scott[25] demonstrates the cost to the nation of antisocial behaviour from childhood through to adulthood. He has developed group parent training programmes using standardised videos, which he has shown to be both cost effective and clinically effective. Unfortunately they are not widely used because of the lack of child mental health services.

Temperament

Temperament is the fourth dimension to be considered. It is defined in Collins dictionary as 'natural disposition, cast of mind, constitution'. Temperament is multifaceted including aspects of the other dimensions. To narrow the focus only two components will be considered: physiological arousal levels and differences in temperament between male and female.

Physiological arousal includes activating mechanisms in the central nervous system (cortical arousal) and in the autonomic nervous system (autonomic reactivity). The autonomic nervous system controls the basic body functions of heart rate, blood pressure and digestion. If it is less stable, there will be excessive reaction to environmental stimuli. The New York Longitudinal Study on infant temperament as a predictor of adult mental health[26] shows how this makes a difference to life chances. Sunny tempered infants who smiled readily, fed and slept well, and adapted easily to change, attracted more positive adult attention. They were more likely to glean whatever nurturing was available. They became better adjusted adults. Fretful infants with less adaptable biological rhythms and excessive autonomic reactivity (eg crying all night) were more difficult to bond with. Adults played and talked with them less. They had a greater risk of adult mental illness.

Another factor leading to intolerance of the physical

surroundings is 'sensory defensiveness'. This is deficient processing of incoming sensations such as from the skin, the mouth and throat or undue sensitivity to noise. How can such children proceed with the tasks of development if they cannot tolerate the feel of clothes on their skin, or food in their mouths, or if they cringe at loud noises? They become 'problem children'. Are they mad or bad?

At the other extreme of this dimension are the various levels of underarousal that are thought to contribute to the development of psychopathic personality disorder (reviewed by Lynam[27]). Lower autonomic arousal, under-reactivity to environmental stimuli, cortical underarousal (shown by abnormal EEGs – electroencephalograms) are findings of an unusual subtype of ADHD.[20] Only occasionally does one see such children in an ADHD clinic. They have a high pain threshold – they break bones and fall into stinging nettles without flinching. They seem to seek out dangerous stimulation to increase their arousal level – such as fire setting or playing chicken on the motorway. They are extremely impulsive, only habituate slowly and do not learn from experience. They seem indifferent to suffering in others and appear cruel and without conscience. But how can someone empathise with pain if they scarcely experience it themselves? It is clear how they would induce adverse responses from all around and how this would reinforce antisocial behaviour. Fortunately Ritalin is effective medication in childhood although boys dislike its effect in flattening their excitement.

Gender differences in temperament

To what extent are the stereotypes of male and female temperament reflections of innate biological differences, genetic and hormonal, or merely the product of social conditioning? Or is there reciprocal interplay in other areas where nature and nurture interact? A teleological argument would say that differences in temperament equipped men and women for different roles in the survival of the species.

Women need to be emotionally available to nurture the children, whereas men, in times past, needed physical courage to defend the tribe. Aggression served better than ready empathy. Eisenberg[28] demonstrated that capacity for empathy was the same in men and women. It was the ease of emotional expression that was different.

Nevertheless stereotypes are apparent in early childhood. Girls appear more intuitive, more empathic, more interested in the subtlety of relationships. Boys are more practical, logical, interested in how the wider world operates. Girls are more biddable and meticulous.

Are these gender traits produced by cultural child rearing practices or do parents simply reinforce what is already there? There is clearly a range of temperaments and parents might try to tame a tomboy girl or shame an effeminate boy. Whiting[29] describes how different cultures socialise their young in different ways. A historical perspective would suggest that present day Western culture favours the 'female' capacity for emotional communication whereas in past eras the male characteristic of aggression was encouraged.

Marked gender differences are found in child development practice. Not only are girls more robust and have a lower infant mortality rate but they show fewer developmental disorders. Autistic spectrum disorders, language delay, dyslexia and ADHD are all four times commoner in boys. In referrals to child guidance clinics of pre-pubertal children, boys predominate largely with conduct problems, whereas in adolescence the gender ratio equalises, because girls present more anxiety and depression. Of relevance to the mad/bad debate is a tendency for boys to externalise problems as aggressive behaviour and for girls to internalise distress.

Zahn-Waxler[30] in her discussion *Warriors and Worriers* describes how this shapes deviant antisocial behaviour in adulthood. Does it follow that men are more 'bad' than women? There are far more men in prison. Moreover rates of ADHD and dyslexia are disproportionately high in the prison population. From a moral perspective, although it seems harder for men to keep the law, deviant psychopathology in women may interfere with their vital role in child rearing (see below) and do just as much harm to society.

Recent research using brain imaging techniques[31] has shown differences in emotional processing and styles of thinking between men and women. It is not simply social conditioning. Men and women are indeed equipped for different roles in life. For instance women are better at identifying emotions in other people. Parts of the brain (the amygdala and the cingulate gyrus) show different rates of neuronal activity when male and female subjects are asked to identify emotional states. Furthermore women respond differently to a challenge. They are more likely to show fear and conciliation compared with the male aggressive response. Male cognitive function (style of thinking) which is logical and practical is also demonstrable neurologically.

An elegant piece of research on Turner's Syndrome,[32] a sex chromosome abnormality, suggests that the female X chromosomes may contribute to these polygenic gender differences in cognitive function. Whereas the normal complement is two sex chromosomes, XX in females and XY in males, Turner's Syndrome has only one X. The genotype is XO. The phenotype is a stunted, infertile girl albeit with normal intelligence. However there is a distinct difference in temperament depending upon whence the single X chromosome is derived. If it comes from the father the Turner's child has better language and executive function and better psychosocial adjustment. If it comes from the mother the child has a much greater risk of autism, ADHD and language disorder.

This poses interesting hypotheses. When the paternal X chromosome is paired by the Y in the normal male does it contribute to the 'male' stereotype – logical, pragmatic (ie good executive function), not swayed by feelings? When it is counterbalanced by the maternal X chromosome, as XX in the normal female, does this favour the 'female' temperament – less logical, more emotional? The same hypothesis would suggest an increased vulnerability to autistic-like cognitive dysfunction when the maternal X pairs the Y.

Mood disorder

The concept of a dimension of mood is not new. However genetic studies suggest two dimensions. One involves drive, social achievement and creativity but carries a vulnerability to manic depressive disorder.[33] The other genetic strain is distinct and produces a neuroticism and vulnerability to unipolar depression.[6] Both are interesting from different points of view for our debate.

Diagnosis of mood states in young children is difficult because they do not present the typical adult picture. Yet major depression can be recognised by behavioural symptoms, withdrawal, misery, failure to thrive, and irritability. Recent research has indicated that mania also is under-diagnosed in children because it is atypical. Rapid cycling mania appearing as disinhibited excitement, hyperactivity or aggressive behaviour is thought to be associated with ADHD.[34] Emotional disorders in childhood, however, are common and do not usually presage lifelong mood disorder.[23] They are often the result of dysfunctional family systems. Introducing appropriate boundaries for containment and control benefits both the insecure demanding toddler and the angry self harming teenager. Nevertheless if family dysfunction is severe enough to produce child abuse and neglect, it yields a bitter harvest of suffering in adulthood (see George Brown's classic work *The Social Origins of Depression*[35]).

Typical manic depressive disorder can emerge as early as adolescence. It is heart-breaking to observe the onset in a teenager who is often a 'good all rounder', excelling in academic, social, sporting and artistic achievement. Mapping the family tree, and indeed the life span of manic depressives shows that strong driving entrepreneurial ability can co-exist with mood disorder, usually separately in different family members but even in the same individual.[33] Some creative artists produce their work either in the context of intense emotion or with the surge of energy of uplifting mood. Spike Milligan, for instance, produced his comedies when 'high' but could do nothing when depressed. Van Gogh ended his life in a state of profound melancholia (psychotic depression).

Fortunately manic depressive disorder is less destructive to the personality than is schizophrenia. Medication is effective both in controlling and preventing the illness. Furthermore there is a wide range in the age of onset from adolescence to mid-life. This allows time for such personalities to bear fruit before becoming ill. This dimension does pose a rather different slant on our debate: 'mad but good', with 'good' meaning 'of benefit to society'.

What is genetic normality?

Statistical normality is defined as within two standard deviations from the mean in each direction (see Figs 2.1a, b and c). Yet, let the reader consider: what proportion of the population is 'statistically normal' on all these different dimensions of mental function – intelligence, empathy, executive function, mood and drive? There are also other, as yet unexplored dimensions such as sexuality and maternal instinct. Are we not all a little 'mad' at times when we cannot stop ourselves being impulsive or disorganised (ADHD) or riding roughshod over the feelings of others (lacking empathy) or being over-sensitive (too much empathy), or letting our moods dictate our actions? Maybe a relative 'madness' is part of the rich variety of humanity? We all need the constraining support of the social group.

It is clearly safer for the individual to be average. However extremes can be understood as beneficial to the population as a whole. We could postulate a selection in the genetic pool, of certain characteristics that at one time were vital for survival. Moderate expression in the phenotype would be advantageous and according to normal distribution (see Fig. 2.1) would benefit most of the population. Extreme expressions (ie the tail ends of the graph), however, are the inevitable corollary for a minority, given the nature of polygenic inheritance. A more clear-cut example from physical medicine is the concept of the 'thrifty gene'. This enables the body to maximise food intake, which would increase survival in famine conditions. In times of affluence, however, diet-related illness, diabetes, obesity and heart disease could occur, especially in the extremes of the phenotype.[36]

A similar hypothesis could be made for autism and ADHD. Mild expressions in the phenotype could have promoted the qualities required in a warrior. These include reduced emotionality, quick reaction times, externalisation of aggression, greater logic. For millennia the capacity for physical combat in men has been necessary for survival. Nowadays these qualities are almost a social disadvantage, whereas the female capacity for emotional intuitiveness is still vital for nurturing the infant.

Some forms of extreme expressions directly benefit society. High intelligence, great drive and creativity, high executive function (eg for managerial ability) are obvious. What constitutes a great leader? Such people can be uncomfortable to live with and even seem failures under normal conditions. Churchill and Shackleton are examples. Even some reduction in empathy if combined with high intelligence can increase logical thought. Thus Einstein was said to have shown Asperger features. A genius is not normal but is nevertheless valuable.

Attachment formation

Genetic endowment is clearly important but so also is the nurturing interpersonal environment in the first year or so of life. If that goes seriously wrong there is lifelong damage to the personality. Recent research (reviewed by Glaser[10]) has demonstrated the neurophysiological substrate for this in the developing infant brain.

All the major theories conceptualising the early development of the mind and personality emphasise the crucial early relationship between infant and mother. Freud describes the 'oral phase' with successful experience at the breast symbolising the 'good object'. Indeed feeding is the chief means of attachment in the infant. The normal process of breast feeding creates the ideal psychosocial environment automatically. Warmth, closeness, eye contact, frequent and lengthy time spent with the infant, all happen without contrivance.

Erikson[37] named the psychological tasks for each of the seven ages of man of which trust must be accomplished in the first year of life. Piaget[38] delineated the cognitive stages of development. He said that the internalisation of the image of the mother is linked to the concept of 'object permanence'. He suggested that the mother's care does not have to be 100% perfect or there would be no spur for the infant to move forward. The concept of 'good enough' mothering was further developed by Winnicott.[39]

John Bowlby's theory of attachment formation is the most practical, stemming from his observations of the effects of institutionalisation in orphanages.[40] He described 'affectionless psychopathy' in the resulting adults who had never had the opportunity as children to bond with a primary attachment figure. As Bowlby said, the infant needs a 'besotted caretaker' to interpret to him what it is to be human. His pioneer work on attachment formation led to major changes in child care policy. Mothers stayed with their children during paediatric admissions to hospital to lessen the trauma of illness being compounded by separation. Foster care replaced Children's Homes. This was the first definitive strategy for preventive child mental health.

Depression in the mother interferes with bonding by rendering the mother emotionally unavailable to the child. The result is an insecure demanding infant (insecure attachment disorder) who can later become hostile and oppositional, particularly if there is no alternative attachment figure. Hostile avoidant attachment disorder is a predictor of adult antisocial personality disorder. Figure 2.3 shows the family dynamics. Father's response to Mother's depression is crucial for the child.

The impact of maternal depression is a preventable child psychiatric disorder whose sequelae last throughout life (see below). Management involves enlisting the father (or grandmother, aunt, etc.) to protect the infant's development by being the alternative attachment figure while the mother recovers. There have been some successful programmes of enlisting experienced mothers in the community to help depressed or vulnerable mothers.[41] The mother needs treatment in her own right for the depression. She also needs help to re-establish her bond with the infant. A study in Cambridge compared the cost effectiveness of three approaches. A short course of eight weekly sessions of interactive work with mother and child was undertaken by health visitors (the cheapest), clinical psychologists and child psychotherapists (the most expensive). The health visitors, given specific training, were just as effective.

Fig. 2.3 Impact of maternal depression on child development

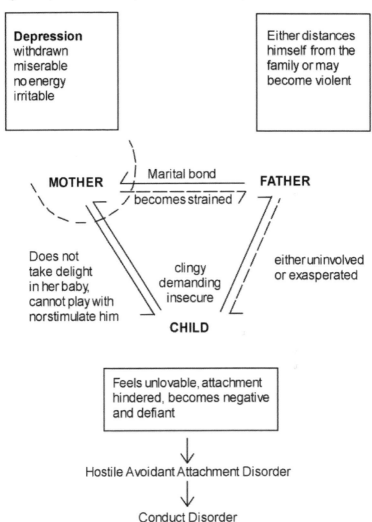

Imprinting by the psychosocial environment upon the infant brain

Recent advances in technology for visualising function of the living brain have made it possible to demonstrate the neurological basis for these theories of infant development. The ERP (event related potential) localises the site of a given mental activity. PET (positron emission tomography) uses radioactively labelled oxygen or glucose to plot areas of the brain responsible for actions, emotions and cognitions. MRI scans (magnetic resonance imaging) and CT scans (computerised tomography) can visualise anatomical structures.

Studies on the effect of child abuse and neglect, particularly in the first year of life, produce some very disturbing findings. There is a lasting imprint on the neuronal networking in the brain, to a great extent irreversible, and producing a permanently damaged personality.

The Maudsley Romanian Orphan Adoption Study is demonstrating that severe stimulus neglect (infants left 24 hours per day unattended in their cots) results in mental retardation, induced autistic defence and attention deficit disorder, and failure of language formation as well as attachment disorder.[42] The extent of damage and its permanence depends on the age at which the neglect ceases. Infants removed at eight to twelve weeks grew up normally. By six months some harm resulted; by nine to twelve months of age there was permanent damage. The worst result was profound imbecility in spite of normal genetic potential. The Maudsley Study is monitoring the extent of 'catch-up' in the cohort of orphans.[43] Tragically this is also seen in child protection work in the UK when parents are unable to provide the most basic care for their infants. These are the worst forms of Significant Harm to child development as defined by the Children Act 1989.

Nevertheless most of the population probably provides 'good enough' infant care so that genetic endowment usually has more influence than faulty neurological imprinting. However this may not be true for the personality disordered or the criminal population.

It is important to realise that we are not simply predetermined by our genes. The early rearing environment has a profound impact on the programming of the brain.

Let us consider the impact of common adverse infant environments such as maternal depression, domestic violence, and drug and alcohol abuse. Drug abuse of course, exerts a dual effect by harming the developing fetal brain chemically, as well as by impairing the mother's capacity to attend sensitively to her baby later on. Glaser[10] reviews the neurological evidence for three types of harm to the infant – deficit of stimuli, distorted experiences and excessive stress.

Normally there is a great spurt of brain growth in late fetal life and in the first year, tailing off by the fourth year of life, resulting in over-proliferation of neurons. This allows for environmental pruning according to usage. Incoming stimuli activate neurons to link up in pathways. 'Neurons that fire, wire.' Unstimulated neurons die. For instance a baby of five months cannot pick up small objects. He simply bats at them. Gradually by trial and error he develops the pincer grip between finger and thumb. The necessary neuronal track is wired up and the skill becomes established. This neural plasticity continues only to a limited extent throughout life, steadily declining into old age. It allows for ongoing learning and adaptation. Skills learnt in childhood such as riding a bicycle or speaking a language are easier to pick up again in later life than to learn from scratch. This is because the neuronal pathways exist; new skills require new neurons.

However certain areas of the brain are genetically primed to 'expect' certain stimuli in infancy.[44] If these are not received the neurons will die. The critical period for vision and hearing is very short, only six months. For instance if cataracts are not removed before six months of age the child will have cortical blindness. More complex developments such as attachment formation and affect regulation (the ability to give an appropriately measured emotional response) are 'expected' by the prefrontal cortex. There is a longer timescale or sensitive period up to three years of age. If the infant does not receive 'good enough parenting' from a carer who can respond to their cues, interpret their needs, comfort and stimulate them, the appropriate neuronal network will not develop properly. The result will be varying degrees of attachment disorder. The depressed mother cannot supply this sensitive, intuitive relationship.

In the normal subject the left prefrontal cortex is responsible for positive approach behaviours and the right for negative withdrawal or aggressive behaviours.[45] With the distorted experience of maternal depression an imbalance results. Such children are found to have over-activity in the right frontal precortex.[46] Their emotional responses are disproportionate. They misinterpret the intentions of others.

Affect regulation does not develop properly because as an infant the child was left unpacified for too long, too often with hunger, pain, cold or even fear. The neuronal pathways which were 'wired up' only allowed for an all or nothing response rather than a measured degree of emotion.[47] Thus the well known clinical picture 'late results of maternal depression' has a neurological basis. Other studies show actual cognitive deficits such as dyslexia and attention deficit in children of depressed mothers.[48]

Thirdly there is the effect of extreme stress on the infant brain. This can follow actual child abuse but also exposure to any trauma, illness, surgery, painful accidents, severe feeding problems (feeding is the chief medium through which attachment occurs). The hypothalamic–pituitary–adrenal axis is the normal mechanism for the fight or flight reaction. It becomes overloaded in the traumatised child resulting in chronically high cortisol levels. Cortisol, which has multiple effects on body tissues, has a destructive effect on neuronal development in overstressed infants. This has been shown to result in reduced brain volume in certain key areas such as the hippocampus, which is responsible for memory.[49]

Child psychotherapists describe how the traumatised child has numerous unprocessed fragments of terrifying mental imagery crowding his inner psychic world. Therapy seeks to link them together in a coherent 'memory'. But this can only be done when the child is removed from the trauma. Cortisol levels in response to stress are lower in a securely attached child who can therefore cope better with stress. It is not possible to treat a child who continues to live in the abusive situation.

Where does the moral responsibility lie for protecting the infant? Can it realistically lie solely with the mother? All too often maternal depression occurs in the context of lack of support and domestic violence. In that case imprinting on the child's brain of stimulus neglect, distorted experience and stress will be compounded. Even if the mother has a simple depression, the father (or the rest of the family) have a vital role to play in mitigating her 'genetic weakness' – as was described above for ADHD.

Sociological changes in society are making this an increasingly difficult problem with contracting family size, mobility of the population, abandonment of marriage, the lower status of motherhood. When extended families lived together there were several potential attachment figures. The nuclear family offers only two. Infants and toddlers in a single parent family are much more vulnerable.[50] The issue of the working mother and crèche-reared children has been much debated. Belsky[51] reviewed the research and concluded that early, extensive and continuous non-maternal care is associated with attachment problems and aggressive behaviour. This might occur when babies are left in the crèche from six am – six pm throughout their preschool years.

The next stage in child development continues the steep learning curve. The parents must begin to socialise the toddler, teach him the skills and habits for life. Erikson[37] sets out the task for the second stage, as 'autonomy versus shame and doubt'. The toddler begins to exercise control; he or she pushes the boundaries, and so learns that he or she is a separate being from mother. Freud describes the oedipal phase when the first concept of sexual differentiation begins. Piaget points out how the little child perceives the world in a concrete, literal fashion (pre-operational and later concrete operational thinking). Extrapolating from the imprinting research, we can say that the complex pre-frontal cerebral association network has not yet developed to allow for abstract thought. Nevertheless the child is learning fast what is safe, permissible and required behaviour. These are the rules of the family system. It is hard work for parents who must be proactive in guiding the child and setting limits. Vulnerable mothers who themselves did not experience 'good enough parenting' find this authoritative task of child management very difficult.[52] Indeed one of the commonest tasks for family therapists for this age group is to put parents in charge of their children. Love is necessary but so also is authority and discipline. Consistency is vital if these 'rules for living' are being imprinted upon the child's brain.

The young child learns self control, respect for authority and concern for others from his interaction with his parents. Maladaptive ways of relating are much more difficult to change later in life. Are set patterns of behaviour reflected in 'beaten tracks' in neuronal pathways? Where does that place the mad/bad debate? How much can conscious effort or will power over-rule such habits? Can the dynamics of the social system facilitate this for the individual?

Significant Harm

'Significant Harm' to child development is a legal term from the UK's Children Act 1989 which sets out the statutory framework for protection of children. It denotes the impact of harmful parenting. British law is adversarial. The onus is to prove that harm has been done before action can be taken. Sadly the law does not facilitate preventive work.

Although the Children Act declares that the needs of the child must be paramount it is all too often the rights of the parents that are most vociferous. Moreover statutory services are starved of resources such that financial constraints must dictate intervention. The threshold for child protection investigation is rising progressively with the decrease in resources. This, in a society where family life is breaking down, is dangerous. Yet society (eg the media) reacts by blaming the social workers instead of empowering, training and equipping them in the responsibility of protecting the next generation.

Social Services must not be seen as part of the 'Nanny Welfare State' but as a vital safety net for children in a complex society where former safeguards have broken down.

George Brown, Professor of Sociology, delineated the abusive experiences and lack of protection that led to learned helplessness. This produces the victim orientation which is an important component in impaired mothering capacity.[35]

Consider the Significant Harm to the social and emotional development of girls from child sexual abuse. It is complex. The physical and emotional aspects of the specific sexual act may lead to post traumatic stress disorder. This can produce a range of psychosomatic, dissociative, depressive, and possibly later gynaecological problems. However, it is the dynamics of child sexual abuse which is equally, if not more, harmful. The abuse of power and trust by the perpetrator, the overt secrecy of incestuous families, and particularly the failure to protect the child by the other significant adults, all combine. The child feels shamed, helpless, exploited, worthless and unloved. This produces the victim orientation. Such girls are ill prepared for motherhood.[52] They have huge unmet emotional needs which they seek to meet through having babies. But bonding is distorted: they cannot provide the sacrificial quality of maternal love. There is a high risk of role reversal with the child meeting the emotional needs of the adult. This in turn shapes the child's personality development adversely. Furthermore abused women lack assertiveness and cannot fulfil the authoritative component of parenting. Moreover they have a tendency to assortive mating whereby they are attracted to violent deviant men who further abuse them. The victim orientation prevents them escaping the domestic violence which further victimises them and their children.

Thus child sexual abuse is a real example of 'punishing the children for the sin of the fathers to the third and fourth generation' (Ex 20:5). A similar tragic pathway can be traced for abused little boys. Research shows that a high proportion of adolescent and young adult perpetrators were victims of child sexual abuse.[53] Huge anger, identification with the aggressor, distorted sexual development as well as the emotional wounding described for girls, all operate to produce the paedophile. Are such men mad or bad? Or should the responsibility for their crimes be shared by those who abused them and failed to protect them? What is to be done about them? Adolescent perpetrators can be treated if they are picked up early enough. However treatment is lengthy and costly. Relapse is all too likely.[54]

Personality disorder

Personality disorder is the most disputed condition in the mad/bad debate. Its origins begin in childhood and it can only be prevented and treated effectively in childhood. Both genetic vulnerability and the rearing environment contribute in the different ways described above.

Significant Harm from deficient parenting is all too often a component in angry, destructive, delinquent or self harming teenagers. They pose a disputed management dilemma to the Youth Justice Department, to Social Services and to adolescent psychiatric services. Are they ill or delinquent, in need of treatment, locking up or specialised therapeutic foster parenting? The turmoil of adolescence can provide a second chance to shape the personality because it is a time of rapid growth and change analogous to infancy. A challenging teenager, however, is much more daunting than a toddler in a tantrum! Integrated, inter-agency adolescent services are vital to tackle this growing problem. They will be expensive. Furthermore, the younger the intervention starts the more effective it will be.

Some degree of Significant Harm can be reversed depending on the timescales of the child and the provision of stable attachment figures, proper nurturing, appropriately structured parenting, etc. Indeed therapeutic fostering is becoming increasingly recognised as a vital form of treatment – certainly an essential prerequisite to effective child psychotherapy. Consider the more subtle aspects of personality disorder such as the devious manipulation of relationships. Any child living in an abusive family must learn survival strategies. Inevitably he learns to manipulate the adults around him, eg play them off against each other, cast the blame on others, induce rejection, take over with a pseudo adult control, etc. If this continues into adulthood the dynamics of interaction become fixed. The experience of relating to normal adults can reverse this in childhood. A child will mirror in the foster family the dysfunctional pattern of relating that developed in the abusive situation. With guidance, foster parents can detect this and set the scene for alternative ways of relating. This recovery is fragile; it takes a long time to consolidate and internalise gains (to realign neuronal pathways?)

Tragically it can be the opposite which occurs. The Significant Harm to personality development can be compounded in foster care. The child, already damaged, is much more difficult to parent, less rewarding and more vulnerable. Foster placements break down; fragile re-attachments are torn apart; tentative recovery is reversed. The policy is to place young children for adoption; yet they have often experienced so many changes before this that the 'sensitive' period for attachment formation is passed. Attempts to reunite them with birth parents, paucity of foster parents, budget restrictions in paying for appropriate therapeutic foster parenting or stark scarcity of skilled experienced social workers all combine to increase Significant Harm.

Significant Harm from child neglect and abuse requires tertiary prevention in terms of damage limitation. A number of strategies exist but all are expensive, 'Quality Protects' seeks to promote best child care practice. 'Prioritising Looked After Children' in terms of education and health services tries to compensate for the lack of kinship that would otherwise do this.

'Concurrent Planning for Adoption' aims to reduce multiple changes of carer for the child. Would-be adoptive parents become the short-term foster parents while attempts at returning the child home are tried. This requires careful planning, selection of cases and skill in the social worker; it is not widely practised.

Private fostering agencies are developing 'Therapeutic Foster Parenting' as a recognised job with a salary, appropriate supervision and support (£300 per week as opposed to £80). 'Spare Grandparents', 'Adopt a Granny' or 'Generation Link' seek to recruit volunteers from the active retired stratum of the population to befriend vulnerable children in disadvantaged families. Sadly these are only limited voluntary projects. Their potential needs to be realised by proper funding in the statutory services. 'Spare Grandparents' could reduce the need for removing the child from its birth family while also protecting from Significant Harm by supporting the struggling mother.

'Sure Start' is a recent initiative attempting 'Primary Prevention' by giving intensive support to 'at risk' mothers and a high quality playschool to 'at risk' children. It is expensive in terms of current children's services but could potentially save millions in crime prevention.

Epidemiology

The epidemiology of child mental ill health is worrying. Findings of key studies[55] show an increase over the past 25 years from six percent to ten percent in the level of child psychiatric disorder. Family breakdown was a significant finding. This demonstrates the effect on the next generation of the factors undermining family life – the high divorce rate, the increasing pattern of sequential cohabitation (or serial monogamy) rather than pair bonding for life, the devaluing of motherhood compared with the high status of the working woman, etc.

The National Child Development study[56] quantifies the effect on child morbidity. Various measures were used such as paediatric outpatient appointments, special educational needs, behaviour problems in school, as well as psychiatric symptoms. Children of single parent families showed twice the rate of these measures, compared with intact nuclear families, step families showed six times the rate, and multiply reconstituted families showed ten times the rate (see Fig. 2.4).

Fig. 2.4 Correlation between family breakdown and child dysfunction (National Child Development Study)

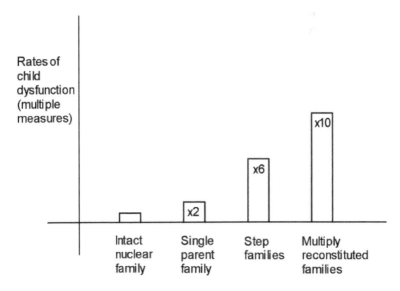

Psychotic symptoms in children

Psychosis is the medical term for madness. In this chapter we have taken a less precise interpretation because in childhood psychotic symptoms have a rather different significance. Psychosis in the adult is defined as a loss of grasp of reality in clear consciousness. Things are seen or heard (hallucinations) or believed (delusions) which the normal person does not perceive as real.

The child on the other hand is still in the process of understanding the real world, developing frames of reference, comprehending the complexity of life. He or she has a rich fantasy life, with much 'magical thinking' (a primitive mental defence mechanism). A healthy child can distinguish between fantasies and reality. He uses pretend games and make-believe to rehearse the adult roles he sees played out before him. Indeed this is a vital part of social learning – but he knows what is 'pretend'. A traumatised child who is not securely parented has a much more tenuous grasp of reality. Because he does not yet have the necessary frames of reference (or cerebral neuronal association networks) stressful life events cannot be processed (made sense of). Traumatic memories re-emerge repeatedly as terrifying 'flashbacks'. These must be dissociated – split off from conscious awareness simply to protect the mind from intolerable stress. If too much of a person's experience is dissociated he or she will indeed have an incomplete grasp of reality.

In clinical work we interpret hallucinations in children according to age, life experience and impairment of function. Thus a four year old who hears voices is probably talking to an imaginary friend. One simply checks that all else is well and reassures the parents. A hallucinated ten year old is more likely to be expressing anxiety about recent stressful life events. The child and family will need help to understand the 'hallucinations' as intense worries and to find ways of alleviating them.

Psychotic symptoms in a teenager have a more serious significance because this is the age at which schizophrenia can emerge. Risk factors for early onset include genetic loading. Hallucinogenic drugs (such as cannabis) can also precipitate genetic vulnerability. Even though it has a clear biological pathology, schizophrenia can be worsened by systemic societal dysfunction either in the family or the suprasystem. Family dynamics characterised by high expressed emotion are harmful. Rapid social change (as in immigrants) increases adaptation demands.

If the child's history indicates Significant Harm from abuse, neglect or chaotic upbringing and there are clear signs of damage to their development, then hallucinations may have a more sinister meaning. Too much trauma has been dissociated. Distorted memories break through in trance-like states leading to behaviour over which the young person has no conscious awareness or control.

Two case histories will illustrate:

Case A

A 13 year old girl had suffered repeated sexual abuse of terrifying variety from her grandmother, her father and two uncles since early childhood. Her mother had also been abused and was unable to protect her. The girl was the eldest of a large number of grandchildren of this grandmother (who had herself suffered child sexual abuse in an orphanage). The girl felt responsible for her younger cousins and tried to protect them by warning the authorities. Unfortunately she was so frightened and intimidated that she could not give a coherent logical account of her abuse in court. Her fragmentary contradictory story reflected the chaos of her inner psychic world and her tenuous grasp of reality. Lawyers did not appreciate that requiring her to testify publicly would overwhelm her fragile defences. The case was thrown out of Court. Social Services attempted to protect her but she repeatedly ran away from foster care. One day she was cradling her five year old brother in her arms when it seemed to her that the child's face became the face of the perpetrator. She pushed a pillow onto the face to smother it. Fortunately she 'came to' in time to resuscitate the child and call the ambulance.

Several more attacks on her siblings occurred during dissociative trances before the situation was understood and she was removed. Once she was in a place of safety the dissociative episodes became florid and self harming ensued. Attempts were made to engage her therapeutically but were thwarted by continuing threats from her family who could not be brought to justice. She longed to have a baby of her own and to work in child care so as to 'regain her lost childhood'. Sadly when she later had her own baby she could not care for it safely. It had to be removed. She

was diagnosed as borderline personality disorder,
a psychiatric cripple, a risk to herself and others.

The second case had a better outcome because the child was rescued young enough and was placed with skilled therapeutic foster parents:

Case B

A four year old boy was taken into care because his young
single mother begged Social Services to take him. She could
not cope with his violence and extreme destructiveness.
She seemed to be terrified of the child. She herself had had
a tragic violent abusive childhood in and out of care. In the
Mother and Baby Unit where she was placed as a teenage
mother, staff strongly advised that the baby be adopted as
the mother could not take responsibility, nor bond with
the child being so damaged herself. However the inner city
Social Services lacked the staff to process the case. Five
years later the child showed the picture of extreme neglect
seen in the Romanian Orphan Study: he could not speak,
nor play, nor socialise; he gobbled food as though starving;
he could not focus attention and was intensely hyperactive.
He was violent and unpredictable and required constant
supervision.

After a year with the skilled foster parents there was
dramatic change. Language had developed and ability
to play with toys – but not with other children; normal
satiety of appetite had returned; he could dress and toilet
himself. He had required constant vigilance and patience
by the foster parents setting limits, reinforcing boundaries,
repeatedly putting him back on track. He required much
structure and routine or he would relapse into chaotic
behaviour. Once speech emerged he talked of voices in his
head telling him to do bad things. This seemed to fluctuate
with the degree of stability in his life. After a holiday
with the foster family and a move to a new school (ie two
changes) the voices became more vivid telling him to kill
the baby (another foster child). He tried to smother it
but was rescued in time. Wise management by the foster
parents, careful separation and supervision of the two
children helped to calm the situation. The threat of adoption

and consequent removal from the foster home was removed
by judicious advice to Social Services. Careful use of
Ritalin also helped. It strengthened his short term working
memory and so enabled him to formulate his thoughts
better, express himself in speech and utilise school.

Systems theory of social function

Consider three models of social system: the healthy model and
two forms which are dysfunctional. The healthy system has clear
leadership which is authoritative but not authoritarian (ie not
despotic), approachable and understanding of the needs of the
members. The hierarchy of the system (ie the natural order of
predominance) is clear and each member knows their place, their role
and what is expected of them, ie boundaries are clear. Yet boundaries
are permeable: there is communication up and down the hierarchy.

Members can expect help and guidance from those higher
up, and also receive approval or discipline. The unwritten rules
governing the system are upheld by the benign leadership. The
unspoken beliefs and expectations of the system are not morbid,
fearful or secretive. The system acts as a buffer to safeguard yet also
to facilitate its members in negotiating their progress through life.

A family is a healthy social system if the parents (or the
patriarch in an extended family) are firmly in charge, have a mutual
understanding in exercising authority, nurturing and direction of the
children, and have a supportive, loving relationship with each other.
The children are free to develop in an age-appropriate way with clear
boundaries yet have warm communication with the parents.

A school is a healthy social system if a capable Head empowers
the teachers, supports their discipline, is readily accessible to
them and creates a positive ethos of high ideals in behaviour and
attainment. Pupils sense these values so that bullying is minimised
and hard work is seen as relevant. Rutter's elegant study, *Fifteen
Thousand Hours*[57] (the average duration of schooldays) was a follow
through of his baseline epidemiological study of Inner London ten
year olds. He demonstrated that the health of the secondary school
as a social system was a crucial factor for the pupils' outcome
independent of neighbourhood, wealth of the school or pupils' own
family background.

Dysfunctional systems

A diffuse system has no clear authority; those lower down the hierarchy have too much power; roles and boundaries are confused and shifting. Values in the system are disputed (anything goes) or harmful (eg over-protective, 'the world is a dangerous place') or are not conducive to the development of members (eg unrealistic expectations).

Schools

Trends in schools in recent years show an increase in behaviour disorder, disrespect for authority and unruly classes. Teachers are threatened at times, even assaulted. Their authority to discipline children is being curtailed yet their duties are being increased – ie they have more responsibility but less power. Parents and even children are encouraged to lodge complaints. Yet teachers are expected to nurture the children and teach values for life – ie to exercise a parental role.

A small fairly frequent occurrence is illustrative. An angry mother storms into a primary school classroom at nine am as the children are coming in and confronts the teacher for reprimanding her child. What would be the effect on teacher and children? Such a thing would have been unheard of a generation ago. Teachers were held in awe. What has changed? Is it the consumerism of society whereby the customer is always right? Is it the blame culture conveyed by the media whereby public servants must bear the responsibility but never the ordinary man? Is it the downside of democracy whereby the voter must be pandered to? Or was this mother an unsupported, depressed, victimised, single mother unable to control her own child and with no-one to offload onto but the teacher?

A sort of system is emerging with unclear authority and confused roles – inevitably a diffuse dysfunctional system. Strong experienced teachers can resist these destabilising forces from the wider system of society (the suprasystem) and establish a healthy school. But it is becoming increasingly onerous. Teachers are leaving the profession. Initiatives of the Education department have further demoted teachers; league tables and OFSTED reports have blamed schools. A systemic understanding of the impact could have led to a more constructive approach.

Could the situation in parts of the USA, where pupils are shooting teachers, be an expression of extreme systemic dysfunction? In developing countries such as Africa, schools have a more rigid system with very strict discipline. Interestingly there is much less conduct disorder but much more anxiety.[58] Parents see education as requiring hard work and discipline.

Families

The diffuse family system is a common dysfunctional model encountered in family therapy. In such a family it is not clear who is in charge, who has the most influence. It may be a small child who can call the tune. The parents do not give clear messages to the children; they often countermand each other's authority; the children learn to manipulate them. Oppositional behaviour develops; relationships are set in a negative cycle.

Another scenario is the child triangulated into marital disharmony acting as a buffer to parental rows. Role confusion and changeable boundaries are harmful to child development. For instance a mother may become over-involved with her child if the husband cannot give her the emotional closeness she craves. The child becomes burdened with emotional responsibility for the mother. This interferes with adolescent separation and autonomy. Several teenage psychiatric problems are related to this family dynamic. Any illness, handicap or adverse life event will further stress a dysfunctional system (eg a child with ADHD, a mother with depression, an unemployed father), whereas a robust system would cope without producing symptoms in its members.

The third model is the rigid system. The parents are dictatorial, inflexible, not in touch with their children's needs and feelings. Boundaries are impermeable, discipline strict. The children may feel inadequate, anxious and unloved. This model is much less common than in former eras when 'children should be seen and not heard'. Political correctness nowadays promotes permissiveness in parents and self expression in children. This favours the diffuse system.

Indeed families do not function as isolated units in society. Just as individuals are profoundly influenced by the immediate social systems to which they belong, so family units are safeguarded or undermined by the suprasystem of society. Value systems, social conventions, moral sanctions and indeed religious beliefs set the framework in which families function in any given culture.

The sanctity of marriage is a fundamental principle in all major religions and cultures. The loss of it in Western society demonstrates how essential it is as a safeguard.

Marriage breakdown

Consider the impact of divorce or parental separation on the family system that came into being as the children arrived. The system is shattered. Attachments are torn apart. Ground rules and boundaries must reform. The children may be leaderless and rudderless for a time as the parents grieve, rage or dispute. Later the single parent, usually the mother, may seek solace in one of the children as confidante who thereby becomes raised in the hierarchy. This burdens the child with responsibility beyond their remit. The mother loses authority over the child; the pseudo adult behaviour of the child distorts his or her own peer relationships.

Later on if the mother takes another partner, this process must be reversed; the child must come down in the hierarchy to give place to the stepfather. Stepfamily dynamics are complex (see Fig. 2.5). Few stepfamilies appreciate the confusion in the child and the need to forge a new family system. If such family disruption happens several times, as it does with multiple changes of partner, it is not surprising the children suffer. Indeed the findings of the National Child Development Study demonstrate ten times the morbidity in children of multiply reconstituted stepfamilies. [59]

Research on the impact of divorce has shown some effects to be mediated through poverty and social disadvantage but family conflict is a consistent finding.[59] Protective factors include the capacity of the parents to form an amicable co-parenting relationship in contributing to their children's upbringing. Minimum disturbance to the children's lives in terms of living in the same house, attending the same school – as opposed to major disruption – also helps. So also does a chance to talk to a third party about their feelings of divided loyalty, anger and grief. Amato[60] has found by follow-through studies that divorce has a lasting impact upon children's lives in terms of less educational attainment, lower income, less marital success and less psychological well being.

The suprasystem of society

The values and dynamics of the suprasystem (be it neighbourhood or national) set the scene for the units of society – such as families and schools – to function. This in turn influences the mental health and behaviour of individuals. Does this give us a clue regarding moral responsibility? Political correctness nowadays asserts that morals are judgmental and distasteful – 'It's up to the individual to decide what's right'. But actually according to Systems Theory it is the system itself which strongly influences the individual's behaviour. What forms political correctness? How can we define it? In systems terms it is the unacknowledged beliefs, the unwritten ground rules of the suprasystem. As our cultural value system, political correctness seems almost to have replaced religion.

Fig. 2.5 Readjustments to family system following parental changes of partner

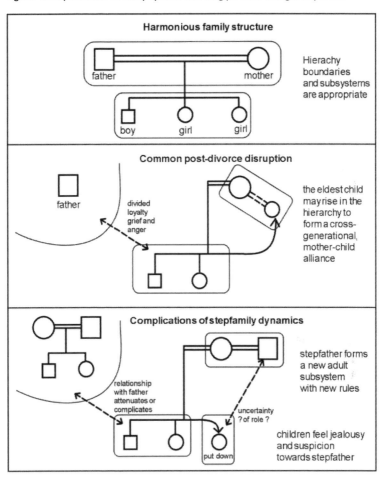

Consider the changes in sexual morality over the past 50 years. Many factors have contributed, such as demographic shifts, birth control, greater longevity, the status of women, career structures, the influence of the media. The previous morality of Western society based on Christianity said that sexual behaviour was only acceptable within the marriage relationship. Of course people broke this moral code but still they recognised the rules. Furthermore anything other than heterosexuality was deviant and immoral. This gave no recognition to the plight of those with abnormal sexual orientation. In contrast the 'politically correct'

view seems to be that individuals are free to express their own sexuality as long as it is not harmful to others. Also, it is acceptable to have several sexual partners as long as they are in sequence.

We need to consider the impact of this change in morality upon society as a 'human ecosystem', the fundamental biological purpose of which is to reproduce the species successfully.

What sort of system is emerging? Is it healthy, diffuse or rigid as defined above? It is certainly not rigid – a totalitarian society is an example of a rigid social system where there is no doubt at all where the power lies. But is Western society a healthy system? There is real confusion as to who holds the power, ie has the maximum influence. Is it the elected government? Big business? The media? It is no longer the Church. Powerfully influenced by the media, which exploits human passions in advertisements and drama, the boundaries of what is socially acceptable are constantly being pushed further away from former norms. What would have been shocking on TV 20 years ago is now commonplace. A system without clear leadership or accepted limits and boundaries but with disputed values is *diffuse*. A diffuse system is not healthy and its members will suffer symptoms and become impaired – ie fail to function, such as the units of society, families and schools.

There needs to be a systemic re-evaluation of the influence of the media. We often hear of research studies into the impact of TV sex and violence on children as individuals. But what is the impact upon the fabric of family life? The boundaries of what is permissible are expanding. The titillation of sexual appetite does not help the self control needed for partners to stay together to rear their children.

We may say that controlling the media is social engineering. But the propaganda is happening by default. Minority groups with a cause seek 'airtime'. Writers traditionally had a legitimate role to make statements on controversial issues from the fringes of society. Nowadays because of the ubiquitous and voracious nature of television this has taken centre stage. Yet it is not representative of the average sensible citizen.

The 'wisdom of the elders', which traditionally had a steadying role in communities, is no longer at the top of the hierarchy in terms of influence. This all seems to be a parody of the freedom of speech. The message conveyed by television is all too often the opposite of what is required to readjust the dysfunctional system – questioning authority, the bad guys win, sexual licentiousness.

Consider the effect on other cultures. American TV and films are widely exported. Remote communities take their message as a literal portrayal, rather than a parody of American life style. The reaction of conservative Islam against the USA could be as much due to the effete licentiousness of television as to political issues. The recent trend towards a severe dress code by Islamic women is probably a reaction to the provocative immodesty portrayed on the small screen.

Human passions need channelling and controlling. If they are exploited instead, they will eclipse the more vulnerable instincts. Thus the dedicated, persevering self-sacrificing roles of parenting or teaching in rearing the next generation need to be ring fenced and protected by the social conventions of society – ie the sanctity of marriage, the authority and prestige of the teaching profession.

If we say that moral responsibility is a vital astringent protective force in society, by what authority are morals ordained and upheld? It has been said by a leading British psychiatrist, Professor Robin Murray, that preventive mental health would require a move from the lectern to the pulpit: By this he meant that scientific and clinical approaches could not supply the moral force that was inherent in religion to enable people to control their behaviour towards each other. Religion informs the moral ground rules of a healthy social system. Political correctness in 'post-Christian' society has dispensed with religion and with absolute moral values. The politically correct view implies that as there are so many extenuating factors explaining a person's behaviour he needs understanding not judgment.

Yet it seems just as meaningless to declare that the individual must therefore be 'mad' and never 'bad' when he or she misbehaves (whether this is law breaking or mundane selfishness). In Systems Theory moral responsibility is binding upon every member of the system, once its precepts (whatever these are) become integral to that system. According to this theory, the system is seen as an organism with interlinking parts, rather than an isolated unit. If a member infringes the rules, pushes the boundaries, the systemic pressures of social conformity will discipline them. Their own weakness will shape the way the group interact with them in a process of circular causality (reciprocal interaction). The expectations of the group (their moral code) will hold him or her in check in a healthy system, or exacerbate the problem in a dysfunctional system. One sees this with ADHD children. The way their parents manage them influences how much the ADHD handicaps them.

In this chapter we have defined 'madness' as that which needs help and allowances made. This was further developed as 'genetic weakness' and 'faulty imprinting'. Everyone needs to be part of a group of some kind so that 'weakness' can be contained and faulty habits disciplined by the structure of the group. Humans are social beings inter-dependent upon one another. As John Donne, theologian and philosopher wrote in 1564:

> *No man is an island entire of itself; every man is a piece of*
> *the continent, a part of the main; if a clod be washed away*
> *by the sea Europe is the less, as well as if a promontory*
> *were, as well as if a manor of thy friends or of thine*
> *own were. Any man's death diminishes me because I am*
> *involved in mankind. Therefore never send to know for*
> *whom the bells tolls: it tolls for thee.*

Interestingly, the ancients, and indeed present day traditional healers in the developing world, have a sounder grasp of the impact of the system than we do in our scientific society with our intense individualism.

The expectations of society in the past protected family life; but we have swept away the moral sanctions that underpinned our social life. It is one thing to break the rules but quite another to dispense with them altogether – that fundamentally alters the system; it becomes dysfunctional. For instance, people may rejoice that illegitimacy no longer carries a stigma. But what have we got instead? Children without their own father continue to be at a disadvantage socially, materially and emotionally.[61] The worst results are becoming evident on inner city estates where unsocialised children roam in gangs not answerable to any adult authority. Stigma, though unpleasant, is protective of society just as pain is protective of the body (eg the painful corneal reflex protects the eye from injury). The stigma of divorce and illegitimacy limited their incidence. The price of sexual freedom in modern society has been the breakdown of family life.

Adolescence

All adolescents must negotiate the values of the suprasystem to reach adulthood. Indeed most intact cultures structure adolescence carefully with rites of passage, clear expectation of career paths and appropriate supervision (for instance chaperones). In such a diffuse suprasystem – as Western society has become – there are few guidelines, little protection and insidious temptation. Expectation to embark upon active sexual life early but in the absence of any supervision leaves young people open to abuse, vulnerable and bewildered. Are young people 'bad' when they become promiscuous and have teenage pregnancies, or has society failed them by removing all moral responsibility? Drug trafficking finds a ready market in a wealthy society with a confused youth having few boundaries. Expectations of material and academic success generate further tension in adolescents. There is no longer a clearly marked pathway to follow their parent's trade. Each generation must forge their own way. It is now much more difficult for young people to become launched in life. Wider choices may be seen as freedom but also generate uncertainty and stress.

In Western societies girls particularly face an emotional dissonance between biological drive and commercial expectations. Now that the social expectations of girls have changed, what happens to the biological makeup that geared them to motherhood? Meticulousness and intuitiveness in relationships can lead to an over-conscientiousness and anxious perfectionism. These features characterise girls with anorexia nervosa. High achieving girls or those burdened with an inappropriate sense of blame or responsibility are most at risk.

A young English girl was asked why she had joined the Islamic faith. She said that as a Muslim she did not have to 'do everything' but could focus upon what she was born for – to be a wife and mother.

Culture bound psychiatric syndromes are becoming recognised as associated with Western industrialised materialistic society. For instance, eating disorders, anorexia nervosa and bulimia nervosa have steadily increased through the last 100 years. Self laceration and para-suicide by overdose are probably further examples. In developing countries these syndromes are rare but different culture bound syndromes can be recognised as equivalent, eg hysteria and brief reactive psychosis[62] (a psychosis of short duration which is often linked with a life event).

Adolescent brain development

Relevant to these adolescent dilemmas and to the lack of supervision and protection afforded by modern society is a growing body of research on development of the adolescent brain. This is demonstrating that the brain, at this critical period, is remarkably neuroplastic and undergoes specific and significant remodelling producing new neural networks and pathways.[63] Moreover this neuroplasticity is experience-dependent. This means that the life experiences of each young person have a unique influence on the programming of his/ her brain and on the current and future patterns of thinking, relating and behaving. Furthermore there is both increased vulnerability to negative environmental experiences and enhanced receptivity to positive ones.

Thus imprinting on the brain of the psychosocial environment is critically formative not only in infancy but also in adolescence. At the start of puberty there is a great surge of growth in grey matter (neurons) followed by steady synaptic pruning into young adulthood. This pruning is important for the fine tuning of sophisticated higher order cognitive functions mediated through the frontal cortex. These include emotional regulation and inhibition of inappropriate behaviour, also the various aspects of executive function such as analysis of problems, decision making and planning for future tasks.

Another vital cognitive function is 'mentalisation'. This is the capacity to distinguish between one's own perspective of a situation and how it might look from another person's perspective, ie to empathise with the thoughts and feelings of others. The synaptic pruning operates on a 'use it or lose it' basis. The frequency and intensity of adolescent experiences determine which networks survive the pruning. It is therefore vital to ensure that those neuronal pathways underpinning adaptive – rather than maladaptive – behaviour grow and strengthen.

However, there is a disparity in the timing of development of areas of the brain responsible for emotional rather than cognitive function. The limbic system which mediates emotional experiences changes rapidly at the onset of puberty, producing powerful emotional urges for sexual behaviour, independence and social bonding – whereas cognitive control processed in the frontal cortex lags behind by several years. Thus the adolescent must cope with intense emotional experiences without the ability (which comes later) to regulate, to contextualise, to create plans for or to inhibit.

This indicates an obvious need for adult guidance and supervision. Yet consumerism, the availability of alcohol and drugs, the expectation of free sex – indeed the modern youth culture – all present great risks. Society must take collective responsibility for the crucial transition of young people into adulthood.

This neuroplasticity of adolescent brain development should afford opportunities for tackling early personality disorders. However, feasible and effective treatment modalities have yet to be developed. The psychotherapy school of thought always maintained that there was another opportunity 'to put things right' in adolescence, although damaged teenagers do not seem to be accessible to straight psychotherapy. 'Therapeutic foster care' is being pioneered by a Maudsley research team.[64] This window of opportunity needs to be grasped.

Influence of religion on the suprasystem

Religion has always been an important determinant of the ground rules of the suprasystem. Religion provided the compelling drive to enforce social sanctions and contain passions. All major religions set out a framework for the meaning of life, the moral authority over mankind and particularly the conduct of family life. The roles and duties of different phases of life are delineated. In this way the upbringing of children and the welfare of the future generation is protected.

Let us consider the Christian blueprint for family life as set out in the Bible. Christianity was one of the foundations of Western civilisation, alas largely forsaken nowadays. However these are the social norms and moral values which political correctness (our new ideology?) is rejecting. The biblical picture of God as Father compares with the authoritative yet loving parent who sets clear boundaries and expectations. God is portrayed in the Old Testament as wrathful, holy and uncompromisingly righteous but also as 'abounding in steadfast loving kindness and mercy'. The Ten Commandments (Ex 20 and Dt 5) set out the moral code. The first three Commandments establish the authority of God. The fourth limits working hours. The fifth and seventh set out family responsibility. The remaining four address social evils. It is interesting that covetousness or envy, jealousy is included. Envy is a very corrosive force in any social system.

Consider the two family related commandments. 'Honour your father and your mother, so that you may live long in the land…' and 'You shall not commit adultery': these set out the mutual responsibility between the generations and between husband and wife. Discipline is seen as an expression of love. In modern society the authority of the parents is often minimised and the loving role emphasised – often to the point of permissiveness. In the practice of child psychiatry and family therapy we often seem to be upholding morals, putting parents back in charge of their children, getting them to set boundaries, telling them their children will be much happier if there is authority in the home. The Bible describes God 'disciplining us as sons'. Hebrews states 'No discipline seems pleasant at the time but painful. Later on, however, it produces a harvest of righteousness and peace' (Heb 12:11). 'If you are not disciplined…then you are illegitimate children and not true sons' (Heb 12:8) (ie not members of the system).

It is interesting to consider the New Testament message in terms of Systems Theory. The sacrificial death of Christ on the cross has seemed a meaningless irrelevance to modern man. Indeed so it did to the intellectual Greeks of the first century ('…foolishness to Gentiles', 1 Cor 1:23). The Bible provides several allegorical pictures to convey the meaning of the Cross – the Paschal Lamb, the scapegoat, the ransom, the curtain of the temple torn down.

God who is righteous and holy has set the rules of the system – rules which are vital for the well-being of society. Yet mankind cannot obey them. Why cannot a merciful loving God simply forgive? He knows the fallibility of man. Could this fallibility or 'weakness of the flesh' be seen as equivalent to the definition of 'madness' in this chapter with components being genetic weakness, faulty imprinting, inculcation of bad habits into brain pathways? In less medical language this could be termed 'irrationality and the inability to do what is morally correct'. However even though man may fail repeatedly God cannot waive the rules – that would change the nature of the system.

The apostle Paul wrestled with the 'mad/bad' dilemma in his treatise to the Romans:

> *I would not have known what coveting really was if the law had not said, 'Do not covet'…Once I was alive apart from law; but when the commandment came, sin sprang to life and I died…I do not understand what I do. For what I want to do I do not do, but what I hate I do…What a wretched man I am! Who will rescue me from this body of death? Thanks be to God – through Jesus Christ our Lord! (Romans 7:7,9,15,24-25).*

> *For what the law was powerless to do in that it was*
> *weakened by the sinful nature, God did by sending his*
> *own Son in the likeness of sinful man to be a sin offering.*
> *And so he condemned sin in sinful man, in order that the*
> *righteous requirements of the law might be fully met in*
> *us....(Romans 8:3–4)*

Thus the sacrifice on the Cross and 'justification by faith' enable God to forgive while upholding the system. Without the mercy of the Cross the church can either have a cruel and damning impact upon society (impose a rigid system) or become weak, ineffectual and irrelevant (contribute to, or identify with a diffuse system).

Consider the positive outcomes of the biblical stricture limiting sex to the marriage relationship. It serves to harness the power of the sexual instinct to energise the family not simply to produce children but to reinforce the parental relationship in rearing them. The role between man and wife is to be complementary rather than competitive. They are to bring out the best in each other.

The New Testament principles for the marriage relationship enshrine the innate differences between men and women which equip them for family life. Thus women are the emotional care-givers; men are the defenders and providers. Ephesians 5 states that the husband is to be the 'head' of the family but is to love his wife 'as Christ cares for the church'. Could we interpret the word 'head' in its systemic sense? A healthy family system requires clear leadership not disputed power. Indeed in family therapy practice if the father opts out and does not take a leadership role, the whole family suffers. However the model of Christ caring for the church is a very high ideal. Christ is depicted as 'a loving shepherd who gave his life for the flock'. There is no place here for a dictatorial husband who forces his wife to obey his every whim. His leadership of his wife must cherish her and empower her so that she can exercise her role as emotional care giver both to her children and others in the community. A woman who gives out emotionally needs to be replenished by her husband.

The sanctity of marriage is an essential pre-requisite. This New Testament model for marriage must have been fairly revolutionary in the Greco–Roman world. It promotes enhancement of the position of women rather than subjugation.

Conflicting belief systems

Different religions structure societies in different ways. They give rise to different ground rules for the suprasystem. Indeed religious wars can be understood as a fight to establish which set of rules will predominate. History has many examples of the bitterness of such conflicts. It has never been easy for differing social systems to co-exist unless there is a dominant alternative system in power. For instance, when the British Raj left India bloody conflict ensued to partition Islamic and Hindu societies. Similar ethnic unrest followed the breakdown of communism in the Balkans and former USSR.

Western industrialised materialistic society is giving rise to a suprasystem that is not governed by formal religious beliefs. Nevertheless it inevitably has an albeit unacknowledged, belief system.

Several studies have looked at the impact of Westernisation on traditional communities, particularly the effect of such cultural dissonance and rapid social change on the mental health of individuals.[65] There are indications that social systems respond initially to rapid social change by an intensification of their beliefs and practices, ie they become rigid systems. This is expressed as fundamentalism, a defence against chaos and confusion. For instance in war torn, famine devastated, disintegrated Afghanistan the Taliban could have been understood as having tried to put the clock back by reinstating rigid fundamentalist Islam.

Racial tensions between immigrant communities and Western societies also involve a clash of suprasystem values, ie cultural dissonance as well as biological, material and educational differences. This is particularly difficult for the adolescents of immigrant communities. They must somehow come to terms with these differences in order to form their own identities.

Practical implications for youth crime

Causes

Let us apply the conclusions of this debate to the vexed question of youth crime. The so called 'feral' children, young thugs who run wild on inner city estates – are they mad or bad? They are likely to score low on the polygenic dimensions of mental health: IQ, ADHD, dyslexia. According to the drift hypothesis the genetically disadvantaged slide down the social scale. Furthermore there is likely to be a high rate of teenage pregnancy, maternal depression and domestic violence on these estates.

Chances of 'good enough mothering' are less, so imprinting on the infant brain will be faulty. Hostile avoidant attachment disorder is a common diagnosis in young delinquents. Family life for them was chaotic, harsh and inconsistent. Their parents often had scant experience of good enough parenting themselves. Parenting skills are learnt in childhood. Moreover the parents are often unskilled, unemployed or impaired by criminality or drug and alcohol abuse. Yet in the eyes of the law they have 'parental responsibility'. So although they score high on many of the 'mad' indices they are deemed 'bad' parents.

Attempts to help either parents or children will be of no avail unless controls are put in place. It is an axiom of child psychiatry that it is impossible to 'treat' children who are out of parental control. The first step is to establish a meaningful system around them rather than their being a law unto themselves. The parents also need the discipline of a strong system to require them to keep house, budget, go to work, manage the kids. But what are the systemic dynamics on these estates? The law of the jungle, a hierarchy of violence and fear, often prevails with the dominant influence being a violent man such as a drug trafficker, sometimes a teenage gang leader.

Indeed some of these delinquent children are inappropriately socialised – to the gang. Their loyalty and social code belong to the gang. This has arisen in a social system where the adults have not been there for them.

In the past the dominant person was typically a matriarch in the days when large extended families lived for generations in the slums, eg the Cockneys of South East London. More cohesive community dynamics existed then. The matriarchs had authority over all the children in their street, and also over the mothers who were failing. It is the loss of this extended family system, and now even of the nuclear family, which is more important than the relative poverty of these estates. There is much worse real poverty in the cities of the developing world.

It takes a strong resourceful mother to rear a large family successfully single-handed with no other adult to help at all. Single mothers on deprived estates are not such. Indeed in terms of a viable human ecosystem single parenthood is not realistic. It is only made possible by financial support from the Welfare State – and that does not supply the essential emotional psychological support that is inherent in an intact family.

Immigrating ethnic minorities coming onto these estates pose different problems. They will not have the same selective criteria.

There is no reason why they should score low on the polygenic dimensions or have chaotic family life.

Many theories exist for why people emigrate – to escape persecution, an enterprising search for a better life, occasionally failure at home, only rarely is it mental disorder. The immigrant community will have their own cultural systems that were adapted for life elsewhere and are unlikely to mesh with the bottom social tier on the estate. Too many different cultural systems on one estate will produce a toxic dysfunctional human ecosystem. For their own health and happiness immigrants would do better living on streets with their own compatriots as long as these did not become exclusive ghettos. Chinatown, for instance, in many big cities has functioned very well.

Action

Research on primary prevention has focused upon the individual child and his family. However the conclusions of this debate suggest that addressing the ills of the community system might help the individuals. In the past this approach has involved improving services, employment prospects, income or the architectural layout of the estate. All these are important but can the psychosocial climate of the community be altered? This is an uncharted field to which the derogatory term 'social engineering' could be applied. Nevertheless a 'systemic diagnosis' of a community would be useful. What are the dominating influences on the estate, the leaders and the prevailing ethos? Are there individuals or households who pose a threat from drugs, intimidation, pornography and criminality? What changes can be made by removing harmful elements (sending the gang leader on a youth training scheme, imposing injunctions or imprisonment, rehousing disruptive families)? Antisocial behaviour orders (ASBOs) were introduced by the UK government under the Crime and Disorder Act (1998) to recognise and try to deter behaviour such as vandalism, joyriding and writing graffiti.

More constructive potential leaders could then be enlisted to plan for the estate. Two projects exemplify both the scale of the problems and the extent of interventions which are necessary.

Project A

Brixton Police initiated a project in the 1990s to 'channel through' young delinquents to appropriate services, the BAR Project (Brixton Against Robbery). Two Afro Caribbean adults were appointed to run it, a young man who had been a gang leader and a competent young nurse. He befriended the boys and she contacted the mothers. A committee of local Afro Caribbean Church leaders supervised. A year later the clinic deemed the project a success but the police thought it a failure because it was choked. The boys were not being channelled through. The Rastafarian ex gang leader found himself acting as a father figure to many boys who had never known a father. The nurse was becoming a support figure to many mothers. The police however could not understand the scale of the problem and the extent of deprivation in the lives of the delinquents.

Project B

Another project which sought to enlist the deprived in creating a mutually supportive community was the Greenhouse Club in Camberwell. It was started in the 1950s by a Christian lawyer as a 'club for unclubbables'. It used the technique of closed group youth work. The same group of a dozen boys met on the same night of each week for five to six years. Gradually the club became a second home. Some boys as they grew up became group leaders; parents became involved. Thirty years later the club was partially a self-help community. Only partially – it was always necessary to have dedicated voluntary input such was the deprivation in Camberwell. Volunteers were recruited for two years from young professionals or students as a form of Christian service. From time to time the Club received government funding. Indeed it behoves local authorities to support local community initiatives of which there are many in the large cities.

Primary Prevention such as the Headstart Project in New York has repeatedly been shown to be effective in reducing emotional and behavioural disorders (see review by McGuire & Earls, 1991[66]). But this is very expensive on a large scale. It is worth drawing upon the conclusions of the research to target appropriately. First, the neediest families, those with most social pathology, are the hardest to engage. Assertive outreach is necessary, ie intervention delivered to the home. Simple parenting skills training courses appeal more to the motivated middle class mothers and can de-skill less confident parents. They do not generalise well to the home from the lecture room.

Direct interactive therapy in the home promoting the mother–child relationship is most effective.[67] Sadly the statutory services, either Social Services or Health, are extremely scant and cannot provide preventive work. Many voluntary projects have been pioneered by concerned charismatic professionals or church leaders. NEWPIN was a successful initiative by a psychologist at Guys' Hospital. It sought to empower depressed victimised mothers by enlisting them in a self help befriending scheme. Promoting childhood resilience factors is another approach. Children can better survive adverse family life if they can find an alternative attachment figure such as a teacher or neighbour. Projects such as 'Adopt a Granny' aim to enlist the experienced parenting resources in the active retired population. This is an untapped potential which should be realised by Government planners. The supply of more traditional foster parents is drying up probably because the generation of women who did not go out to work is passing. 'Spare grandparents' could be a more acceptable alternative.

Conclusion

The conclusions of this section of the debate carry a number of implications. First, society as a whole must carry the moral responsibility, cascading from the top down, for protecting the mental health of the next generation. As the old Indian saying goes: 'It takes a whole village to rear a child'. The mother must be the 'besotted caretaker' of the infant in those crucial early years when imprinting is at its maximum. How much should the State assist, for instance by increasing maternity leave to reduce crèche rearing of infants?

The father has a crucial role in supporting the mother and, with her, forming the family which is the microcosm of society where the child's personality is shaped. The father should represent authority, 'headship', so that the child learns control and respect, ie becomes socialised. Both parents need the constraints of the wider family and local community to require them to fulfil these roles. Social conventions, indeed shame, act to limit the 'madness' and 'badness' factors not only in individuals but in families. It is the ethos of society, its cultural values, that determine this. There can be 'mad' and 'bad' families which have catastrophic effects on their members.

Western industrialised society has become complex and unstable. The genetically disadvantaged gravitate to the bottom. They accumulate in grossly dysfunctional communities such as slums or inner city estates. Social evils abound and family life is chaotic. This results in the phenomenon of street children or unsocialised gangs of children. Significant Harm to personality development is high. Yet the moral responsibility lies with the rest of society, indeed the moral imperative. Social dysfunction can affect and even infect the rest of society as drug abuse and crime. There are obvious implications for proper resourcing of statutory services for child protection, children's mental health services and indeed preventive interventions. This includes a systemic understanding of the impact of the media upon the population. Management of the media is much more than simple censorship. It warrants a Government department.

The second set of implications of this analysis of child development concerns the nature of individual moral responsibility. It was beyond the remit of this chapter to discuss the philosophy of free will. Instead the structure and functioning of the human ecosystem is of more immediate relevance to the mad/bad debate and indeed to the practice of child psychiatry. However, this does not imply that the individual has no free will: he or she is constrained by their genetic endowment, their place upon the polygenic dimensions of mental function, their early attachment relationships and how life experiences become imprinted upon their brains. Nevertheless it is our daily experience that we can and do exercise free will and moral choice, albeit imperfect and swayed by the above factors. For some people right and wise choices will be much more difficult and they will need the constraints of the social group.

Others who are well endowed in these various dimensions would be the leaders who supply the strength and direction to social groups. These people will carry greater moral responsibility: 'From everyone who has been given much, much will be demanded' (Lk 12:48).

Does this child development perspective throw any light on the nature of human fallibility? It is clear that no one is perfect.

Everyone has a greater or lesser degree of 'mad' or 'bad' factors. For instance impulsivity is a feature of ADHD, but everyone must resist some degree of it. Constant vigilance can overcome temptation but clear-cut rules enforced by the social system, 'Thou shalt not ...', also help. This poses questions both for the non-religious and for religious people. The former need to consider the impact upon society of rejecting absolute moral authority. Is it enough to rely on 'basic human goodness and common sense'? Yet this does not imply that mankind is all 'bad' any more than all 'mad'.

Religious people need a more robust grasp of these psychological concepts. For too long there has been a mutual distrust, a polarisation, between psychiatry and religion. Religious people fear that a psychological approach will 'explain away' their faith. Mental health professionals suspect that troubled people may be using their faith as a defence against facing their problems. Indeed it is possible to have a 'neurotic relationship with God', to see him as we want to see him, 'in our own image' as it were.

'Neurotic' in this context means that one perceives other people not as they really are, but in the light of an earlier dominating relationship (the imprinted image). For instance, if one's father had been violent one might see all men as potentially violent regardless of the evidence. Previous experiences, unmet needs or yearnings will colour our relationship with God. We might invest in our faith in God what we need psychologically. Indeed religious faith can become inextricably bound up with the mental defence mechanisms of the mind. The more primitive of these defences such as denial, 'magical thinking' and regression lead to our 'kidding' ourselves. We avoid facing painful or arduous issues. At best faith becomes an anxiety management strategy. At worst we project our problems onto others; impute to others our angry, negative feelings (projective defence). This makes it much more difficult to forgive others. The mature believer in Christ learns to empty themselves, pour out their sense of helplessness, bare their soul to the mercy of God. Repentance enables them to let down their defences before God, to accept the healing power of forgiveness, to allow the Spirit of God to empower. Can the Holy Spirit change dysfunctional brain pathways? This is what we believe.

Many interesting questions are posed that must be discussed in another chapter of this book. What is the nature of sin in psychological terms? What should we understand by Christ's teachings on the 'ethic of inner intention'? ('You have heard that it was said, "Do not commit adultery." But I tell you anyone who looks at a woman lustfully has already committed adultery with her in his heart.' Mt 5:27-28.) Hopefully this child development analysis will supply some useful information for such a discussion.

3

Treatment approaches for those with antisocial personality disorders, psychopathy and for sex offenders

M Dominic Beer

In this chapter, the causes and types of personality disorder and psychopathy are described and the issue of moral responsibility is also discussed.

What is personality disorder? What is meant by the term 'antisocial personality disorder'?

What is known about the causes of these disorders?

Are they inherited?

Are they caused by upbringing or are they under the individual's control?

What is society's contribution to those with personality disorder?

How should society manage this group of people?

What is meant by the term dangerous and severe personality disorder?

Do people with antisocial personality disorder warrant treatment? Is there treatment available?

How should antisocial personality disorder, psychopathy and paedophilia be managed from a Christian point of view?

How should the church manage those with an antisocial personality disorder?

What should Christians know about paedophilic sex offenders? How should churches manage such offenders?

What is personality disorder?

Since the famous German psychiatrists, Karl Jaspers'[1] and Kurt Schneider's[2] writings, the field of psychiatry has differentiated personality disorder from mental illness. Illness involves an absence of health for the individual patient. Personality disorder does not imply illness, but is defined by behaviour: 'deeply ingrained maladaptive patterns of behaviour'.[3] These must be present since before adolescence and should lead to the individual, or those they come into contact with, experiencing distress. The disorder, then, is *part* of the personality of the individuals themselves. This is in contrast to the person who has an *illness* which is regarded as having a recognisable onset. The illness schizophrenia, for instance, has been shown to cause a personality change after adulthood has been reached. The symptoms of many mental illnesses can be treated with medication. Personality disorder is often more difficult and complicated to treat. However, the eminent British psychiatrist Kendell[4] has argued that the distinction between personality disorder and mental illness may be difficult to sustain, especially if effective treatments can be found for personality disorder.

Types of personality disorder

There are eight main categories of personality disorder according to the *International Classification of Diseases*.[3] The main features of these eight are:

1. Antisocial: criminality and impulsivity; lack of guilt; failure to learn from adverse experiences; self-centredness and failure in personal relationships. The American Psychiatric Association[5] stipulates that conduct disorder must have been present (antisocial behaviour in childhood).

2. Histrionic: self-dramatisation; craving for novelty and excitement; self-centredness in personal relationships. It is more common in divorced and separated men and in women is associated with suicide attempts. In men it is associated with substance misuse and in women with unexplained medical conditions.

3. Emotionally unstable: impulsive behaviour including criminality; unstable relationships; anger; suicidal behaviour; uncertainty about personal identity; persistent boredom. It is commoner in younger people (19–34 years), women and Caucasians. It is associated with poor work history, being single, urban areas. It is found in patients who also have substance misuse, phobic and anxiety disorder, and has a nine percent suicide rate. In forensic samples it occurs in people who also have antisocial personality disorder. Most studies find that it is co-morbid with lifetime depression, that is to say that people with emotionally unstable personality disorder may also suffer from depression at some point in their life.

4. Paranoid: suspiciousness; sensitivity; distrust of others; argumentative and litigious. This is more common in men of lower socio-economic group, and more common in relatives of patients with schizophrenia. In criminal samples it is often co-morbid with antisocial personality disorder and associated with violent crime.

5. Schizoid: introspection; emotionally cold; detached; difficulty expressing emotion or making intimate friendships. It is uncommon in clinical settings but more prevalent in criminals where it is commoner in men. There is some association with schizotypal personality disorder. Some authorities[6] believe it to be a developmental disorder, possibly in the autism/Asperger's spectrum.[7]

6. Obsessive–compulsive: rigidity in views; lack of adaptability to new situations; perfectionism; indecision. It is more common in white, male, highly educated, married and employed people. It is co-morbid with anxiety disorders.

7. *Avoidant (anxious):* anxiety; ill at ease in company; fearing disapproval or criticism; cautious about new experiences. It is co-morbid with dependent personality disorder and social phobic disorder.

8. *Dependent:* compliant; falls in with the wishes of others; avoids responsibility; lacks self-reliance. It is co-morbid with borderline personality disorder – in some studies it is thought to be the outcome of early social processes in the family environment.[8]

The American Psychiatric Association adds two further disorders:[5]

9. *Schizotypal:* odd beliefs; eccentric behaviour; no close friends; odd speech; inappropriate affect; suspiciousness; excessive social anxiety; ideas of reference; unusual perceptual (15%) experiences. It is common in relatives of schizophrenic patients. There is an association with schizophrenia and it is included in the schizophrenia category in *ICD-10*.[3]

10. *Narcissistic:* Reacts to criticism with rage; takes advantage of others; grandiose sense of self-importance; believes own problems are unique; fantasies of success; sense of entitlement; requires constant admiration; lack of empathy; preoccupied with feelings of envy. This is not found in *ICD-10*.[3] It is diagnosed more in men and in criminals where it is co-morbid with antisocial personality disorder.

The frequency of personality disorder

This varies from 4.4% to 13.0% of the population depending on the study.[8] Of the ten types of personality disorder there is a wide range for each disorder with most having a rough estimate of about one percent.

In the American Classification[5] the disorders are grouped into clusters.

A: Paranoid, schizoid, schizotypal ('odd' group).
B: Antisocial, borderline, histrionic, narcissistic ('antisocial').
C: Dependent, avoidant, obsessive–compulsive ('anxious').

It is cluster B that mainly concerns us in this chapter.

The causes of personality disorder

Borderline personality disorder

Childhood abuse and neglect are very common in these patients with up to 87% having experienced childhood trauma of some sort; 40–71% have been sexually abused; 25–71% physically abused.[9] These statistics raise important theological questions about human accountability, because these individuals have suffered at an early stage from the abuse of other people.

The earlier the abuse occurs the more serious the consequences. Patients with borderline personality disorder have difficulty modulating emotion. They find it hard to think about and effectively manage their own feelings and thoughts – and those of others. This finding has been linked to the difficulties in inter-personal relationships, also to the impulsivity of these patients and their self-harming activities. Often they do not experience pain if they cut themselves and this is linked to the dissociated states where people appear to be cut off from their feelings. Because these states are also found in Post Traumatic Stress Disorder (PTSD), borderline personality disorder is often associated with PTSD.

Antisocial personality disorder

Genetic influences. Moran[10] writes that definitive evidence is lacking but 'most twin and adoption studies suggest that antisocial behaviour (crudely defined in terms of criminal convictions) is associated with a moderate degree of heritability. There is also evidence for a substantial degree of genetic–environment interaction in the genesis of antisocial behaviour.'

Environmental influences. Moran[10] enumerates the following as important: (1) childhood conduct disorder; (2) childhood hyper-activity, and quotes Farrington's work on predictors of future criminality:

1. Socio-economic deprivation.
2. Poor child rearing.
3. Antisocial family members.
4. School failure.
5. Impulsivity.
6. Antisocial child behaviour.

Farrington writes:

> *Offenders differ significantly from non-offenders in*
> *many respects, including impulsivity, intelligence,*
> *family background, peer influence, and socio-economic*
> *deprivation…The precise causal chains that link these*
> *factors with antisocial behaviour, and the ways in which*
> *these factors have independent or interactive effects, are*
> *not known, but it is clear that children at risk can be*
> *identified with reasonable accuracy…It is plausible to*
> *suggest that there is an antisocial personality that arises*
> *in childhood and persists into adulthood, with numerous*
> *different behavioural manifestations, including offending.*
> *The typical delinquent – a male property offender – tends*
> *to be born in a low income, large-size family and to have*
> *criminal parents. When he is young, his parents supervise*
> *him rather poorly, use harsh or erratic child rearing*
> *techniques, and are likely to be in conflict and to separate.*
> *He tends to have low intelligence and poor attainment at*
> *school, is troublesome, hyperactive and impulsive, and*
> *often truants. He tends to associate with delinquents.*
>
> *After leaving school, the delinquent tends to have a record*
> *of low status jobs punctuated by periods of unemployment.*
> *His antisocial behaviour tends to be versatile rather than*
> *specialised. He not only commits property offences such as*
> *theft and burglary but also engages in violence, vandalism,*
> *drug use, excessive drinking, reckless driving, and sexual*
> *promiscuity. His likelihood of offending reaches a peak*
> *during his teenage years and then declines in his twenties,*
> *when he is likely to get married or cohabit with a woman.*
>
> *There is continuity over time in antisocial behaviour, but*
> *changes are also occurring. It has often been found that*
> *about half of a sample of antisocial children go on to become*
> *antisocial teenagers, and about half of antisocial teenagers*
> *go on to become antisocial adults.*[11]

Rutter concludes:

> *We know a good deal about the variables that are*
> *statistically associated with antisocial behaviour but*

*we know less about the mechanisms involved. The
important risk factors for antisocial behaviour include
the temperamental characteristic of impulsivity, low
intelligence, poor parental supervision and adverse
parenting, parental criminality, memberships of the
delinquent peer group, large family size and low family
income, and opportunities for crime.*[12]

These facts suggest interacting elements of both nature and
nurture, both of which have theological implications. It seems clear
that Christians can, and should, try to act to reduce the environmental
influences that reinforce antisocial and criminal behaviour and it is
important to say that not all children with these risk factors go on to
have antisocial personality disorder. From a Christian point of view
there is always the possibility of redemption and repentance.

Psychopathy

This concept goes back to the late nineteenth century and the 'theory
of degeneration'. The French Catholic psychiatrist, Benedict Morel,
combined the biblical concept of the fall of man with early Lamarckian
inheritance and sociological theory. He held that congenital diseases
such as cretinism (hypothyroidism due to lack of iodine in the
local environment, so-called 'Derbyshire Neck' in England), were
attributed to 'generational' or 'degenerational' factors. The theory
of transformational heredity became popular. Because of immoral,
criminal or addictive (eg alcoholism) behaviour in one generation,
the next would suffer mental illness and the successive one from
dementia, epilepsy and very severe mental disorders, often with
physical signs. In Germany it was thought that the nerves ('neuro')
and the mind ('psycho') were affected by such a disease process
('pathy') hence the terms 'neuropathy' and 'psychopathy' came into
being. 'Psychopathic' meant 'psychopathological'. Koch, in 1891,
under 'psychopathic' inferiorities grouped abnormal behavioural
states, including antisocial behaviour, and stated it was due to
degeneration. The famous psychiatrist Emil Kraepelin differentiated
'manic-depressive insanity' and 'dementia praecox' (later to be known
as schizophrenia) from the other 'psychopathic states'. These were
then renamed as the abnormal personalities by his pupil Schneider.
His ten 'psychopathic personalities' were a subclass of the abnormal
personalities and referred to those 'who themselves suffer, or make

society suffer'.[2] These have been modified by the *ICD-10*[3] and are now called personality disorders. So, confusingly, under Schneider's term 'psychopathic personalities', all the personality disorders were categorised, including those where suffering was only experienced by the patient and not by others, eg anankastic (obsessive–compulsive). Now, fifty years later, psychopathy only refers to conditions in which others are made to suffer.

Hare's 'psychopathy checklist' as summarised in Hart and Hare[13] is a 20-item questionnaire which involves scoring the individual 0 (absent), 1 (possibly present), or 2 (definitely present) on the following criteria:

1. Glibness/superficial charm.
2. Grandiose sense of self-worth.
3. Need for stimulation/proneness to boredom.
4. Pathological lying.
5. Cunning/manipulative.
6. Lack of remorse or guilt.
7. Shallow affect.
8. Callous/lack of empathy.
9. Parasitic lifestyle.
10. Poor behavioural controls.
11. Promiscuous sexual behaviour.
12. Early behavioural problems.
13. Lack of realistic, long-term goals.
14. Impulsivity.
15. Irresponsibility.
16. Failure to accept responsibility for own actions.
17. Many short-term marital relationships.
18. Juvenile delinquency.
19. Revocation of conditional release (from prison).
20. Criminal versatility.

Psychopathy is not synonymous with antisocial personality disorder or conduct disorder, but is an extension of both. Consequently only one third of patients with antisocial personality disorder have psychopathy.[14] Much of the antisocial behaviour shown by people with psychopathy is focused on goals such as achieving money, status and sexual opportunities ('instrumental learning'). Sims[15] writes that the lack of empathy is the primary disorder. There is a defect in the capacity to appreciate other people's feelings, especially to comprehend how other people feel about the consequences of this person's own actions. A normal person is prevented most of the time, by shame, or by the capacity for empathy, from carrying out unpleasant actions towards other people. They do not want to be disliked and feel very keenly how it would be passively to be the recipient of such behaviour. It is this inability to feel for themselves the discomfort that others experience as a result of antisocial activities that appear to be absent in the psychopath.

Blair[16] postulates that such people have not learned that this kind of behaviour leads to distress in the victim: 'The emotional impairment found in individuals with psychopathy interferes with socialisation such that the individual does not learn to avoid antisocial behaviour' (p.5) and 'learning to avoid committing moral transgressions involves committing a moral transgression and then being 'punished' by the aversive response of the victim's distress' (p.5). (This Blair calls 'aversive conditioning'.) Blair relates both defects in aversive conditioning and instrumental learning to disorders of the brain, notably of the amygdala and the orbitofrontal cortex. This may fit in with the finding that individuals who have had frontal lobe brain damage develop aggression. Also those who abuse amphetamines chronically have disturbed orbitofrontal cortical regions.

Causes of psychopathy

Coid[17] refers to a study he performed looking at 243 people in a Special Hospital detained under the legal category of psychopathic disorder and also prisoners in special units in prison. Over half (53%) had Antisocial Personality Disorder (ASPD). Overall, although of men in special prison units 86% had ASPD, 69% overall had Borderline Personality Disorder (BPD) and 91% of the women had BPD. ASPD was also associated with paranoid, narcissistic and borderline personality disorders.

Association with other conditions:

1. 50% of all individuals had a lifetime prevalence of depressive disorder.
2. BPD was particularly associated with mood disorders.
3. ASPD was associated with a lifetime history of substance misuse.

In England confusion was caused by the 1959 Mental Health Act defining 'psychopathic disorder' as a legal entity: 'a persistent disorder or disability of mind (whether or not including subnormality of intelligence) which results in abnormally aggressive or seriously irresponsible conduct on the part of the patient, and requires or is susceptible to medical treatment'.

It is interesting that a word such as 'irresponsible' is used since this has the connotation of being 'responsible to another person or to a code of behaviour'. Indeed Schneider[2] remarked that Koch's original main classificatory intention of antisocial behaviour had been 'moral' rather than scientific. This leads to another controversial description of psychopathy which has been criticised as being 'uncomfortably close to a moral concept'.[18]

Types of responsibility

1. Moral and spiritual responsibility. The Bible teaches that each of us will need to give account of ourselves at the Day of Judgment. We will need to give an account of our actions and how we have used the abilities, talents and gifts given to us. This is true for Christians and non-Christians. Even those who have not heard of Christ will still be judged. Paul states that people are without excuse, 'since what may be known about God is plain to them, because God has made it plain to them. For since the creation of the world God's invisible qualities – his eternal power and divine nature – have been clearly seen, being understood from what has been made, so that men are without excuse' (Rom 1:19–20). Christians have been saved and brought into the loving presence of God by means of faith in the saving blood of Christ on the cross. But as Christians we will still need to stand before God and take responsibility for what we have done in our lives. It is noteworthy that this type of responsibility is towards God and only he can judge. He will do so in the future, but he has laid down clear indications as to the criteria he will use to judge us. However, there is also a biblical relativity of accountability. People will be judged not on the basis of what they know, but on the basis of their response to what they know (Lk 12:47–48; Rom 2:14–16; Jas 3:1).

I will explain in more detail later (see chapter four) how the biblical view appears to be one of proportionality. Scott Peck[19] develops this in his discussion of the concept of evil, as encountered in his psychiatric practice. He sees the fundamental disorder as being narcissism. Here the individual is self-centred, lacking the capacity for empathy or seeing things from another's point of view. It is noteworthy that the *Diagnostic and Statistical Manual of Mental Disorders*[20] includes narcissism as an example of personality disorder. It is often co-morbid with ASPD.

Peck quotes the theologian, Martin Buber, who described this phenomenon as narcissists having only 'I–I relationships'. In the book of Genesis, Peck writes that God's acceptance of Abel's sacrifice implied a criticism of Cain. Cain felt diminished and less than Abel. Since he refused to acknowledge this imperfection, he took the law into his own hands and eliminated the object (Abel) which he perceived as the cause of his bad feeling. 'We can see, then, that their narcissism makes the evil (persons) dangerous not only because it motivates them to scapegoat others but also because it deprives them of the restraint that results from empathy and respect for others…As it gives them the motive for murder, so it also renders them insensitive to the act of killing.'[21] Peck writes that evil people attack others instead of facing their own failures. 'The central defect of the evil is not the sin but the refusal to acknowledge it.'[22] Facing and taking responsibility for one's actions is therefore a crucial aspect of the maturity (completeness, perfection) in Christ, of which Paul speaks (Col 1:28).

Peck takes the view that evil is not a matter of degree. He says that we are all sinners, in that we 'miss the mark' or 'fall short'. We however recognise our sin, ask for forgiveness and receive it. We are the 'poor in spirit' (Mt 5:3) whereas the proud in heart think they are without sin. They are unwilling to suffer the discomfort of self-examination (1 Cor 11:28; 2 Cor 13:5). Peck gives the example of the Pharisees who were proud, and who committed evil by eliminating Jesus the good man who showed them up. He became a scapegoat.

Peck sees evil 'as the exercise of political power, that is the imposition of one's will upon others by overt or covert coercion – in order to avoid…spiritual growth'.[23] It is not, however, necessarily only political power that is exercised. Moreover the type of power and its degree will surely depend on the intelligence of the individual. Highly intelligent people may be able to achieve their ends without usually having recourse to violence, whereas the less intelligent may use violence more frequently.

Erich Fromm is quoted by Peck:

> *The longer we continue to make the wrong decisions, the more our heart hardens; the more often we make the right decision, the more our heart softens – or better perhaps, comes alive. On the one hand there is each step in life which increases…my capacity to choose the desirable alternative, until eventually it becomes more difficult for me to choose the undesirable…on the other hand, each act of surrender*

and cowardice weakens me, opens the path for more acts of
surrender, and eventually freedom is lost.[24]

This implies that all cultures are not equal, and that morality is not relative. There are local expressions of certain universal values that make for happier and 'prosocial' people. Likewise, there are aspects of life that are common to all people who are destructive, morally, socially and psychologically. Such people can be said to be psychologically 'branded' or 'seared' (1 Tim 4:2) by the form and content of their beliefs and practice.

From a biblical viewpoint the Apostle Peter's exhortation seems to provide the theological foundation for these ideas:

> *His divine power has given us everything we need for life*
> *and godliness through our knowledge of him who called us*
> *by his own glory and goodness. Through these he has given*
> *us his very great and precious promises, so that through*
> *them you may participate in the divine nature and escape*
> *the corruption in the world caused by evil desires.*
> *(2 Peter 1:3–4)*

God has given us the resources – namely his promises – to combat evil. Peter then exhorts us consciously to choose to 'strengthen' the good qualities in ourselves:

> *For this very reason, make every effort to add to your*
> *faith, goodness; and to goodness, knowledge; and to*
> *knowledge, self-control; and to self-control, perseverance;*
> *and to perseverance, godliness; and to godliness, brotherly*
> *kindness; and to brotherly kindness, love. For if you possess*
> *these qualities in increasing measure, they will keep you*
> *from being ineffective. (2 Peter 1:5–8)*

Christians are not, therefore, called to be passive, but active. True believers are under grace. But grace does not absolve the believer from active responsibility for the consequences of their salvation, but to work it out in fear and trembling (Phil 2:12–13) and in co-operation with God's Holy Spirit (Rom 8:26–29, NEB).

It is these kinds of qualities that will help us persevere and keep on doing good to the end of our lives: 'Therefore, my brothers, be all the more eager to make your calling and election sure. For if you do these things, you will never fall, and you will receive a rich welcome into the eternal kingdom of our Lord and Saviour Jesus Christ.' (2 Pet 1:10–11)

By contrast the Apostle James shows what can happen when we choose wrongly:

> *When tempted, no-one should say, 'God is tempting me'.*
> *For God cannot be tempted by evil, nor does he tempt*
> *anyone; but each one is tempted when, by his own evil*
> *desire, he is dragged away and enticed. Then, after desire*
> *has conceived, it gives birth to sin; and sin, when it is*
> *full-grown, gives birth to death. (James 1:13–15)*

Sin destroys and, if indulged in continually, ultimately jeopardises the possibility of return (Heb 6:4–8, 10:26–39).

God in his love will seek to woo us back to him but:

> *There can be a state of soul against which Love itself is*
> *powerless because it has hardened itself against Love.*
> *Hell is essentially a state of being which we fashion for*
> *ourselves: a state of final separateness from God which is*
> *the result not of God's repudiation of man, but of man's*
> *repudiation of God, and a repudiation which is eternal*
> *precisely because it has become, in itself, immovable. There*
> *are analogies in human experience: the hate which is so*
> *blind, so dark, that Love only makes it the more violent…*
> *so with the soul and God;…sloth which is boredom with*
> *divine things, the inertia that cannot be troubled to*
> *repent, even though it sees the abyss into which the soul is*
> *falling, because for so long, in little ways perhaps, it has*
> *accustomed itself to refuse whatever cost it an effort.*[25]

2. Criminal responsibility. One is criminally responsible 'if the state can prove beyond a reasonable doubt that the defendant's behaviour satisfied the charge and no affirmative defence of justification or excuse can be established'.[26] This type of responsibility depends on the laws of the particular society in which the individual lives and the way in which the judicial system interprets these laws.

What is regarded as antisocial in one society may not be regarded as such in another. Head hunting in the former tribes of Borneo; child sacrifice in the Aztecs; mass murder in Nazi Germany, Stalinist Soviet Union or Pol Pot's Cambodia are regarded as criminal by most other societies. Grey areas occur with, for instance, abortion, which until relatively recently was treated as a criminal offence in most societies, but its legal and medical sanction is now widespread.

In England and Wales the concept of 'diminished responsibility' has been recognised since the Homicide Act of 1957. It had been well recognised in Scotland since 1867. The Homicide Act states: 'where a person kills...he shall not be convicted of murder if he was suffering from such an abnormality of mind (whether arising from a condition of arrested or retarded development of mind or any inherent cause or induced by disease or injury) as substantially impaired his mental responsibility for his acts'.

Thus, the onus of deciding on criminal responsibility seems to have been given to psychiatrists if they are asked whether the defendant is suffering from 'an abnormality of mind'. However, how are they ultimately to define this? In the case of Byrne, a man who strangled a girl after breaking into a women's hostel in Birmingham, abnormality of mind was defined in 1960 as 'a state of mind so abnormal that the reasonable man would term it so'. This suggests that it is left to the jury to decide in the case of murder. If it can be said that juries represent the culture from which they spring, then 'what a reasonable man' would define as 'insane' (itself a legal term) must be culturally relative. This must have an effect on the definition of 'abnormality of mind' held by juries, for sin has deeply affected the minds of all people (Rom 7:13–20). Christians therefore may well have a responsibility to stress what a Christian who is thinking biblically, rather than what a 'reasonable man' would regard as a state of insanity. Barkan[27] has shown convincingly that Western people are highly ambivalent in their attitude to morality. They want morality as a safeguard to injustice, especially as regards their personal and cultural rights, and thereby as a means to the 'moral high ground', but resent being told what to do for the larger national good. Christian responsibility overrides a concern with individualism, seeking what is good for both the accused and society. Some have agreed that Christians are increasingly coming to see the administration of the law as being concerned not with retribution, but with restitution and healing for both parties. Justice is 'restorative'.[28]

In English law, for people who are convicted under the Mental Health Act, criminal responsibility is not emphasised as greatly as it is in the United States of America. In England and Wales the mentally ill who commit a criminal act can receive a conviction and receive a Hospital Order. The degree of criminal responsibility is not put to the test in percentage terms.

In the United States of America there is much more emphasis on degrees of responsibility.[29] In Sweden criminal responsibility is not affected by insanity so it is not an excuse. It merely alters disposal – treatment rather than punishment.[30]

Some professional writers introduce the concept of moral culpability: 'for criminal responsibility there must be "moral culpability"'.[31] Griew[32] believes that mental responsibility (and by extension, criminal responsibility) contains the moral element of reduced culpability. Culpability has to do with blaming and possibly punishing. In summary, in England and Wales (and Sweden) a person may be found to warrant treatment rather than punishment and no blame may be attached.

3. *Phenomenological responsibility.* Sims[33] enumerates six situations which he looks at from a phenomenological point of view (what the person himself feels):

1. The person feels responsible but the action is based on delusional thought and most observers would not consider the person guilty of the consequences of his action because the latter resulted directly from the delusion, eg the person believed he is in communication with the sun and needs to take his clothes off and is charged with indecent exposure.
2. The person feels responsible for an action but actually did not perform the action at all, eg people who confess to murders they did not commit.
3. A person feels responsible for his activity, and is responsible, eg getting dressed or other normal activity. This can also be the case with a psychotic person who is asked why he hit another patient and says 'I don't like him'.
4. A person does not feel responsible for his action for psychotic reasons. A schizophrenic man poured a bowl of porridge over another patient, against his will because he was made to do this by someone else (passivity experience). As in 1. above most observers would not hold him responsible.
5. 'A person denies responsibility for his action, but is responsible. This is conceptually the most difficult situation. For instance a young man with dissocial personality disorder, while co-habiting, injures a woman's 2 year old daughter from a previous liaison. The man claims, through his counsel, that he is not responsible because of his own extremely deprived upbringing and his consequent personality disorder.

However, it is his own volitional act and, even if an outside observer could predict his action, it would still remain his action, his responsibility, and ultimately voluntary ... of course, extenuating circumstances should be taken into account during court proceedings, but the phenomenological aspect of responsibility should not be denied.'[34]

6. A person may not feel responsible for their action and is not responsible. A train driver who runs over a person committing suicide on the railway line should not be held responsible.

Legal issues

Compulsory treatment of antisocial personality disorder

The issue of compulsory treatment of those with ASPD is a vexed one. In England and Wales both the Mental Health Acts of 1959 and 1983 have permitted treatment for psychopathic disorder if it is 'likely to alleviate or prevent a deterioration of (the patient's) condition' and 'that it is necessary for the health and safety of the patient, or the protection of other persons'.

There has been reluctance on the part of mental health services to accept such patients for treatment: 'the stipulation concerning psychiatric treatment is unrealistic, since most patients with psychopathic disorder are not susceptible to psychiatric treatment'.[35]

In England and Wales a vigorous debate on this subject has taken place during the period of the introduction of new mental health legislation. One particular high profile case – the brutal killing of two people by Michael Stone, a man with personality disorder who was not admitted to a psychiatric hospital – has led to proposals to detain those who have not committed crimes but are judged to be of high risk of violence. This has become known as Preventative Detention. Where this appears to differ from current legislation is that currently such people can be detained for treatment only if they suffer from mental illness, psychopathic disorder or mental impairment/severe mental impairment (the latter two broadly speaking correspond to learning disabilities). The new legislation allows such detention for treatment for the much wider category of mental disorder. Critics (eg Mullen[36]) point out that there is a suspicion that the British Government, in order to meet the European Convention on Human Rights legislation criteria to detain those who pose a danger to the public, need to have such persons diagnosed as of 'unsound mind'. It is unclear what the new legislation will be. Both the critics[37] and the Government agree that persons with dangerous severe personality disorder require management and it is to this vexed topic that I shall now turn.

High risk offenders with personality disorders

Coid[8] helpfully provides a table (see Table 3.1) outlining the risk factors for the causation and perpetration for high risk offenders with personality disorders.

Table 3.1

Stage	Age	Risk factors
A	*Childhood*	
	Temperament	Genetic
	Oppositional defiant disorder	Prenatal, perinatal
	Attention deficit with	Family environment
	hyperactivity disorder	Central nervous system integrity, IQ
	Conduct disorder	Poverty, housing
B	*Late childhood/adolescence*	
	Escalating delinquency	Few protective factors
	Peer-group problems	Physical/sexual abuse
	Emerging borderline features	Family disruption/criminality
	(mood and behavioural	Neighbourhood/peer/school
	disturbance)	influences
	Psychosexual maladjustment	
C	*Early adulthood*	
	Persisting criminality	Pattern set by earlier factors,
	Criminal lifestyle/versatility	maintained by:
	Substance misuse	Criminal subculture
	Poor work record	Imprisonment
	Relationship difficulties	Social isolation
	Sexual deviations	Anti-establishment attitudes
	Hierarchical appearance of	Lack of alternatives and skills
	Axis I disorders	
D	*Mid-life*	
	Career criminality	
	Psychopathy (high Hare	
	Psychopathy Checklist	
	PCL-R score)	
	Multiple Axis I disorders	
	(mental illnesses as	
	defined in DSM IV)	
	Repetitive, pervasive	
	antisocial behaviour	
	Institutionalisation in secure facilities	

Strategies for intervention and prevention: Stage A*

If young people can be helped before their antisocial behaviour is ingrained this would be an important preventative intervention. Conduct disorder has been identified as a high risk predictor of antisocial personality disorder affecting four to ten percent of children.[38] It is associated with Attention Deficit with Hyperactivity Disorder (ADHD). In adulthood 40% have serious psychosocial disturbances, including substance misuse, major mental disorder, higher risk of mortality and ASPD.[39] Coid suggests the following primary prevention strategies:

1. A targeted approach to those identified as at high risk of developing adult ASPD.
2. Specific targeting of those with conduct disorder.
3. Prevention of passing on antisocial behaviour from one generation to another by targeting high risk families.
4. Prevention of the development of conduct disorder by attempting to intervene at an earlier stage, ie in pregnancy, infancy and pre-school[40] through families, directed at parenting[41] and in schools.[42]

Social policy and personality disorder: Stages B and C

The social environment helps produce conditions that lead to a higher chance of the presence of risk factors for conduct disorder: breakdown of social cohesion as family and social networks disintegrate; loss of parental figures and lack of adult supervision; frequent moves of home and school. Wallace and Wallace[43] argue that it is wrong to believe that these conditions can be confined to the inner city environments. Thus, it would be a false economy not to spend money on economic and social regeneration. This is further discussed in Rutter[12] and Rutter and Smith.[44]

From a Christian viewpoint, it is clear that Christians need to be active in bringing the Gospel in both word and in action to these communities and in putting pressure on policy makers and fund holders for appropriate interventions. The problem is that moral concern seems at present to be invested in groups that are able to protest the loudest, and those declared mentally ill or criminally insane are often the least able to do this, as they do not represent a

---

* This is explored further in chapter two

distinct cultural group.[27] Governments want to be seen to be taking the moral high ground, and these groups do not appeal to the general public in this way. Rather they rouse the public's ire. Some Christians, nonetheless, may be called to represent those groups in whom there is no public investment designed to gain votes. Who will organise the criminally insane or severely personality disordered – when they themselves are not able to do so – but those whose concern is for the most rejected and despised? Surely Jesus is the model for the Christian, who used the despised Samaritan as an example of the neighbour, and the crucified thief as the one who could find salvation then and there? Some practical examples of Christians being involved might include Christians visiting those in prison and the work of the Salvation Army amongst the homeless, many of whom have personality disorders and mental health problems.

Stage D

Once an individual has reached this stage the patterns of behaviour are deeply ingrained. The approach adopted by the British Government has come in the wake of psychiatrists and psychologists not wishing to admit such patients to their treatment settings. What are the reasons for this reluctance?

1. In order for any treatment to be effective it is likely to be lengthy given that the behaviour is ingrained.
2. Lengthy treatment requires commitment on the part of patient and treating professional. Patients tend to drop out or disengage if difficult issues arise. This is especially likely in voluntary treatment. If treatment is compulsory on the other hand the measures needed to enforce it may need to be considerable. It may be possible only to provide it in very secure settings from where the patient cannot escape.
3. If one is imposing treatment against a person's will and depriving the person of liberty, the principle of reciprocity indicates that the treatment should have a chance of success. The problem with many treatments is that the research evidence is often lacking to show the effectiveness of the treatment.

Coid[8] writes that there are a number of prerequisites that are needed for a programme to be implemented successfully:

1. Effective communication concerning all aspects of the programme to all levels of personnel involved in programme delivery.
2. Development of procedures and administration to ensure effectiveness.
3. Allocation of financial resources.
4. Development of monitoring and data systems for evaluation.

In England and Wales, the Government circulated a consultation document.[45] A Home Office project team was appointed to establish a number of pilot projects in prisons and maximum secure hospitals. Coid[8] points out that the 'treating arm' of the policy – the Department of Health – was not sufficiently involved. The stage has not been reached where proper evaluation can occur because the policy is not co-ordinated.

The proposals on Dangerous and Severe Personality Disorder (DSPD) to be evaluated are:

1. To ensure that dangerous people with severe personality disorder are kept in detention for as long as they pose a risk to others.
2. To provide high quality services to enable them to deal with the consequences of their disorder, reduce their risk to others, and to work towards successful re-integration into the community.

Coid[8] writes that these objectives lead to the following testable measures of the effectiveness of services:

1. How effective are the new assessment processes in identifying individuals with severe personality disorder who pose a risk to the public?
2. How effective are they in identifying when those individuals no longer pose a risk?
3. How effective is treatment within the new services in reducing risk and promoting re-integration into the community?

However, these are difficult for the following reasons:

1. The definition of severe personality disorder has not yet been fully clarified.
2. How is 'significant risk' to the public defined?
3. How accurate is the screening instrument to detect risk?
4. How many people posing such risk are there?
   How many false positives and false negatives are likely?
5. Where should they be treated?

Coid and Maden summarise the interface between the criminal justice system and the health service:

> *Multiagency public protection panels led by police and probation already operate a model of regular review and community surveillance of individuals posing a high risk. Multiagency public protection panels should be recognised as the primary source of community referrals for future mental health assessments under new legislation. But few trusts have so far identified resources to ensure a mental health professional on more than a handful of panels.*

> *Psychiatric interventions cannot influence offending rates at the population level as the problem goes far beyond mental health. But psychiatrists could contribute towards targeted risk reduction in subgroups of individuals identified on the basis of previous criminal behaviour. Future risk management must shift from unrealistic over reliance on mental health legislation towards a new hybrid whereby criminal legislation becomes central. Revision at this stage may be unpalatable. But we risk misplacing ultimate responsibility onto the wrong professionals who will fail.* [46]

What is treatability?

Adshead[47] compares the treatability of those with psychopathy or mainly cluster B antisocial personality disorders, to treatability of patients with physical conditions. Treatability is a function of:

1. The nature and severity of the disorder. Adshead[48] writes that the term 'severe personality disorder' has been in usage for over 30 years and is not a modern political invention. She writes that there is some evidence that milder personality disorders are more amenable to treatment. If there are a number of personality disorders present together then the treatability is diminished.

2. Degree of spread of the disorder. This refers to the number of systems that have become involved with the individual such as healthcare, social, criminal justice. Also important are the frequency, variety and harmfulness of any risk behaviours.

3. *Co-morbidity.* The presence of other disorders such as learning disabilities, mood or substance misuse disorders may diminish treatability.

4. *Whether and when the disorder is identified and diagnosed.* The earlier it is recognised the greater the treatability.

5. *Personal strengths and weaknesses of the individual.* The early experiences, especially having formed an attachment with another person, will make treatment easier. The current family and social support is important. According to this model then, there appears to be a kind of 'sliding scale' of treatability.

Tyrer in his favourable commentary on Adshead's paper also advocates a more positive therapeutic approach: 'It is therefore very convenient to use complex arguments and weasel words to avoid taking on the responsibility for caring for a population that yields few rewards and many brickbats. The question doctors and other health professionals have to ask is, if we do not treat, or at least manage the care of people with personality disorders, who else will do it more successfully? Currently, the answer is a deafening silence and I personally feel, although I recognise the counter-arguments, that we are best placed to carry out these responsibilities. (p.416)[49] John Gunn (former Professor of Forensic Psychiatry) has made the observation that: "If psychiatry gives up all its difficult patients, society will give up psychiatry and there is no doubt that society is looking towards us, perhaps rather desperately and despairingly, for a lead. I also suspect that we have treatments for personality disorder that are effective but have not yet researched them adequately. In any case, dealing with people who have personality disorders can be rewarding and is certainly challenging, and once successful treatments are available, the diagnosis will lose its stigmatising label, just as depression did all those years ago."'[50]

There are strong arguments for viewing the person with ASPD if not as the 'weaker brother' (Rom 14; 1 Cor 10:28) at least as analogous to such a brother. Such people, if possible, should not be exposed to further temptation to which they are vulnerable. However hopeless, and however short one's attempts at the construction of a restorative environment may fall, this appears to be the Christian option.

6. *Resources available for treatment.* If those responsible for providing treatment do not believe treatment will help, this will have an adverse effect on an individual who, from their upbringing, will most likely have had difficulties in interpersonal relationships. As Adshead writes: 'It is very unlikely that many individuals with personality disorders will be 'treatable' in facilities that require them to be obedient, compliant, passive and grateful.'[51] She writes that the parallel with cancer can be given whereby in specialised units the treatments can be effective.[52]

7. Scientific research. The state of research on personality disorder has many gaps in it with regard to both causation and treatment. Adshead cautions against either a too optimistic or a too pessimistic approach and quotes Rudyard Kipling's poem: 'If you can meet with triumph and disaster/and treat those two impostors just the same.' Tyrer quotes Hillaire Belloc's description of a young woman with a personality disorder:

> She was not really bad at heart,
> But only rather rude and wild,
> She was an aggravating child.[49]

A Christian view of 'psychopathic' offenders

A Christian psychiatrist who has had first hand experience of managing some of the most 'psychopathic' offenders in English prisons, Dr Bob Johnson, writes: 'untreatability has gained a sickening hold on academic psychiatry...If you agree with the psychiatric establishment that it is entirely justifiable to label personality disorders as "untreatable" then you should be aware of the parallels with leprosy from an earlier era'.[53] He says that the patients he was treating were traumatised in childhood and had not been able to access the normal social support that others have. 'During my five years working in Parkhurst Prison...I was treating the most dangerous severe personality disorders (the notorious DSPDs), too violent for Broadmoor, and in every one of the 60 murderers and the six serial killers, there was a grievous wound, or perceived wound from long ago...During my five years in Parkhurst Special Unit the number of violent assaults recorded, dropped from one every two months to one every two years. Tranquilliser usage fell from 3.6 kilogrammmes a year to 150 grammes. No alarm bells were rung for 2.5 years – a unique record world-wide for any Maximum Security Prison Wing'.[54]

Johnson emphasises the application of spiritual values – truth, trust, consent – in all his interactions with his patients. He believes that the root of this socially destructive behaviour is that these men knew no better because of their upbringing. He 'took it as axiomatic that every human being is born loveable, sociable and non-violent. This is what I found to be the case there.[55] "Hannibal Lecter resembles a real serial killer as little as Donald Duck does a drake. All real people are human beings underneath. If you can ever contact their deeply buried humanity, then, and only then, can you being to assist them in pulling themselves together."'[56]

It requires people with attributes such as patience, firmness, discernment and empathy to achieve this, but the Christian view is that no-one is irredeemable, other than those who quite specifically have decided on a prolonged course of criminal and antisocial activity after discovering that there is a better way, and then decisively rejecting this way. While God wills that all should be saved, and none should perish but should instead come to repentance (2 Pet 3:9), nonetheless many will not do so, for narrow is the way, and few there are that find it (Mt 7:13–14). Johnson writes: 'Nothing I have written ever condones what dangerous individuals do. Three murderers in Parkhurst threatened to kill me. Nor do I shrink from locking "mad axe men" up temporarily, to protect society'.[57] As evidenced in the principles found in the Old Testament, the community must be protected, but in the New Testament the approach appears to be that of Jesus' saying: 'neither do I condemn you...Go now and leave your life of sin' (Jn 8:11).

A similar application of these views can be seen in the work of Jackie Pullinger[58] in Hong Kong amongst the drug addicted people. Although she conducted no formal research, her results working with damaged people, using a loose therapeutic community model, can serve as an inspiration and cause for hope that anyone can receive healing and come to repentance and faith in Christ. Similarly, work with the mentally ill being done by Holmes and Williams in Christ Church, Deal, UK, consciously taking a therapeutic community model, suggests that this is a powerful instrument for change.[59] The proviso here is that people are willing to become committed to a journey of change. This being the case, those committed to such a journey then discover a new identity that is acceptable to both themselves and others, first in the therapeutic community, and then in the wider world. Crucially, the community has to be accepting of the outcast, and have a genuine and not merely an academic understanding of where these hurt people have come from. The Christian message provides a story through which the person's biography can be understood. This biography is no longer a mere chronologue of events, but a story, with structure, plot and direction. It thereby provides the potential for healing, and being made new. Meaning and purpose arise from the ashes of lives that were felt by some to be worthless.

Johnson's approach is also reflected in that of Newell,[60] the Governor of an English prison committed to treatment of prisoners (Grendon Underwood Prison). He quotes the Office of National Statistics for England and Wales: 78% of male remand prisoners have a personality disorder, 64% of males sentenced do and 50% of female prisoners do. The most common was antisocial (63%, 49% and 31% respectively). For female prisoners, borderline was the commonest.

Because of the need to have a prison functioning in as orderly a fashion as possible, the authorities screen those who are predicted to be disruptive. The Hare psychopathy checklist is more predictive than a diagnosis of ASPD. 'The task with this group is damage limitation, minimising damage to themselves, damage to fellow prisoners and damage to staff.'[61] This is crucial, as a community cannot be therapeutic if there are those who are felt by the group to be destructive of the journey towards positive change within the group (eg see Williams[59]).

Newell outlines four main therapeutic areas available in a long prison sentence:

1. *Cognitive therapy-based.* The Sex Offenders' Treatment Programme, Thinking Skills and Reasoning and Rehabilitation Programme have led to a 10–15% reduction in re-offending in the community. There are also reductions in measures of the denial of offending, reductions in pro-offending attitudes (for example distorted thoughts about effects on victims) and predisposing personality factors (ability to be intimate, low self-esteem).

2. *Therapeutic communities.* An example of this form of therapy being employed in the English prisons is at Grendon Underwood. The principles of group therapy are applied to the prisoners and 'there is an emphasis on the exploration of the tensions and issues that arise in the process of living together in a community in a series of group settings, during which residents build up and explore relationships in the "here and now" with co-residents and staff, and as they progress through treatment begin to take on responsibility for managing aspects of the environment. There is an egalitarian emphasis, with the hierarchy flattened, and an encouragement of free communication between.'[60]

3. Behavioural therapeutic elements where incentives and earned privileges are used as a reward for appropriate behaviour.

4. Rehabilitative elements – progress through the prison service to the community via Parole Board, Probation and rigorous risk assessment.

A recent publication by the National Institute for Mental Health in England (NIMHE) outlines 'Treatment in Forensic Settings for Personality Disordered Offenders':

Thinking Skills
- Programmes include Enhanced Thinking Skills (prison service), Think First (probation service) and Reasoning and Rehabilitation (multiple use).
- Group programmes comprise between 40 and 80 hours of treatment contact.
- Treatment goals include beginning to enhance self-control, inter-personal problem solving skills, social perspective taking, critical reasoning skills, cognitive style, and an understanding of the values which govern behaviour.
- Brief focused training of multi-professional groups is emphasised, in order to ensure treatment integrity and consistent programme delivery.

Dialectical Behaviour Therapy
- A modified version of DBT, for use with men with a diagnosis of antisocial personality disorder, is currently being adapted for use by high secure personality disorder services.

Anger/Violence Management
- Recent evaluated programmes for personality disordered offenders in secure health settings include social problem solving, and a Violence Risk Programme.
- The RAID ('Reinforce Appropriate, Ignore Difficult and Disruptive') approach for working with extreme behaviour is based on improving and strengthening

interpersonal relationships; it is being piloted in high
secure personality disorder services.

Sex Offender Treatment Programmes

- Accredited sex offender treatment programmes (SOTP) take
  place in prison and the community; additionally, multi-agency
  programmes have been developed to meet specialist needs,
  such as for adolescents or personality disordered sex offenders.
- Programmes are based on a cognitive-behavioural model of
  treatment, which involves:
    - recognising the patterns of distorted thinking which
      allow the contemplation of illegal sexual acts,
    - understanding the impact which sexually abusive
      behaviour has on its victims,
    - identifying key triggers to offending as an aid to
      relapse prevention,
    - reducing recidivism has been shown to be contingent
      upon the level of deviancy demonstrated by the
      offender, and the duration of treatment
      (between 100–200 hours).

Forensic Psychoanalytic Psychotherapy

- The stated aim of treatment is to help free patients from
  the more self-destructive ways of feeling, thinking, and
  behaving and so to enable them to live and function more
  easily in the community.
- Staff are multi-disciplinary, but all have undertaken
  further training as psychoanalytic psychotherapists or
  psychoanalysts.
- The model emphasises consultation and support in forensic
  services…Eclectic long-term approaches, such as group and
  individual therapy, psychoanalytical and the inclusion of
  family members in treatment programmes, have been found
  to be highly effective.[62]

At a community day-to-day level, the World Health Organization has
given advice on management of antisocial personality disorder.[63]

1. Ensure that the individual's reason for seeking help has
   been clearly identified…
2. Begin from the standpoint that the majority of requests
   from the individual are legitimate…

3. Take as full a history as possible...
4. Do not accept all information at face value...
5. Aim to create an open and trusting relationship...
6. Set clear limits...
7. If the individual presents with genuine symptoms of a mental disorder then he or she should be offered treatment...
8. Do not expect to like these individuals...the skill lies in accepting these demanding and potentially unpleasant individuals without accepting their demanding and unpleasant behaviour...
9. Assist with problem solving strategies for crises...
10. Do not expect to be able to 'rehabilitate' these individuals ... approximately 50% of individuals who appear to have met criteria for an antisocial personality disorder in their teens or twenties will no longer meet criteria after the age of 30, with 80% no longer meeting criteria at age 45...those 20% who do not remit remain a serious problem for society.

Regarding item eight – one needs to draw a distinction between 'liking these individuals' and Jesus' injunction to 'love your neighbour'. One can surely help people without necessarily liking them.

The last item is paradoxical. While it may well be true that the specific individual concerned may not find resocialisation, these figures suggest that the majority do in fact find a measure of adaptation to society.

On the basis of an exhaustive literature review, Warren *et al*[64] have made the following recommendations for developing treatment services for severely personality disordered people who act dangerously:

1. Consideration should be given to employing the Therapeutic Community model for those with personality disorder within high security settings.
2. Where use of the Therapeutic Community model is impractical – for example where individuals are unable or unwilling to voluntarily enter a pure Therapeutic Community treatment programme – consideration should be given as to what, if any, aspects of the therapeutic model can be applied within the particular unit.
3. The application of a Therapeutic Community model should not exclude the use of other treatments, eg drug therapy,

dialectical behavioural therapy (DBT) and therefore within this therapeutic, a range of the other treatments could be employed.

4. Consideration should be given to the use of DBT particularly for the reduction of self-harming behaviour.
5. The application of DBT for self-harming behaviour in men should be explored.
6. Pharmacological treatment should be used for symptom reduction, taking the evidence for each drug into account.
7. Physical treatments (psychosurgery) for personality disorder should not be employed save as absolute last resort when all other treatment options have been tried and found to fail.
8. Other 'composite' treatments such as the partial hospitalisation programmes should be considered for adaptation to higher levels of security.
9. A range of treatments should be available at each level of security to allow individuals to move through levels of security with consistency of treatment approach.
10. The long-term pathway of care should be considered such that service development provides for both geographical and conceptual proximity of treatments delivered at different levels of security.

Dolan and Coid[65] provide four case histories that exemplify the difficulties inherent in many of the assessment and treatment methods. In one survey[66] conducted by patients themselves, they were asked: 'What would you say are the things which have helped you most?' The answers shown in Table 3.2 were provided. That 'family' was given the greatest priority is significant in the light of Guinness (see chapter two in this book).

Table 3.2

Family	36%
Therapists	34%
Advocacy	34%
Medication	26%
Voluntary centres	24%
Psychiatrists/hospital keyworker	24%
Community Mental Health Team	22%
GP	14%
Friends	14%
Other patients	10%
Church	10%

Patients interviewed by NIMHE[67] summarised helpful and unhelpful features of personality disorder services as in Table 3.3.

Treatment of borderline personality disordered patients

Psychotherapy

According to randomised controlled trials, the two main approaches are dialectical behavioural therapy (DBT) and psychodynamic psychotherapy.[68] DBT is based on the principle that Borderline Personality Disorder (BPD) is essentially the result of deficits in interpersonal and self-regulatory skills and these skills can be taught in therapy. It is a special adaptation of cognitive therapy which employs a manual. It includes a functional analysis of behaviour and also intensive support from the therapist – empathy, validation of feelings, and management of trauma. This may also include out of hours telephone contact with the therapist. Both DBT and psychodynamic psychotherapy have three key features:

1. Weekly meetings with an individual therapist.
2. One or more weekly group sessions.
3. Meetings between therapists for consultation/supervision.

It is suggested that treatment needs to be for at least one year, and probably longer. Other common features include: the building of a strong therapeutic alliance with the patient to withstand the frequent emotional storms; specific goals are often formulated; clear

boundaries; empathic approach to the abuse suffered; help patients
to take responsibility for current behaviour; not too much emphasis

Table 3.3

Helpful features for personality disorder services	
Early interventions, before crisis point	Good assessment/treatment link
Specialist services, not part of general MH	Conducive environment
Choice from a range of treatment options	Listens to feedback and has strong voice from service users
Individually tailored care	
Therapeutic optimism and high expectations	Supportive peer networks
Develops patients' skills	Shared understanding of boundaries
Fosters the use of creativity Respects strengths and weaknesses Good clear communication	Appropriate follow up and continuing care Involves patients as experts
Accepting, reliable, consistent	Attitude of acceptance and sympathy
Clear and negotiated treatment contracts	Atmosphere of 'truth and trust'
Focus on education and personal development	
...can make people feel respected, valued and hopeful	

Unhelpful features for personality disorder services	
Availability determined by postcode	Rigid adherence to a therapeutic model in cases where it becomes unhelpful
Office hours only	Passing on information without knowing a person
Lack of continuity of staff	Long-term admissions
Staff without appropriate training	Use of physical restraint and obtrusive levels of observation
Treatment decided only by funding/ availability/diagnosis	Inappropriate, automatic or forcible use of medication
Inability to fulfil promises made	Withdrawal of contact used as sanction
Critical of expressed needs (eg crisis or respite)	Dismissive or pessimistic attitudes
Staff only respond to behaviour	
Staff not interested in causes of behaviour	
...can make people into 'career psychiatric patients'	

on the past, although appropriate linking of the here and now to the past can be helpful; flexibility on the part of the therapist is required.

NIMHE[67] recommends that specialist teams be set up, the members of which have a common treatment model and who are committed to the patient for at least one year. Day patient services would also be provided.

Drug treatments

The American Psychiatric Association[68] states that SSRI antidepressants and low dose antipsychotics have the best evidence for helping symptoms.

Therapeutic communities

Patients treated at The Henderson Hospital show a clinically significant change in their symptoms one year after discharge.[69] Bateman and Fonagy[70] have also shown that patients with BPD responded well to psychoanalytical therapy combined with inpatient care. Overall, Winston concludes: 'Despite many unanswered questions, recent developments give ground for optimism. It is now difficult to sustain the view that all borderline patients are untreatable. The outlook for this challenging group of patients may be starting to improve'.[9]

In the church it is often this group of patients who are most problematic to help because they appear to demand so much time, energy and emotion. Guiding principles of working with this group of patients should probably be based on the above WHO guidelines[63] along with those outlined in the treatment chapter. It is important to work with the mental health services where possible.

Paedophilia

This is defined as a sexual preference for children usually of prepubertal or early pubertal age. It is not co-terminous with antisocial personality disorder or psychopathy. However the presence of antisocial personality disorder is a poor prognostic sign. Craissati[71] writes that there appear to be two groups of abusers:

1. Men who had been abused themselves as children; experienced emotional difficulties and abuse as children; engaged in sex play with boys as children; self-harmed and received psychological help as adults; engaged in sexual contact with other men; abused male children.

2. Men who had previous sexual convictions and tended to use physical coercion and to abuse strangers.

Explanation of child sexual abuse

Finkelhor[72] wrote that four pre-conditions need to be met for abuse to occur:

1. A potential offender who is motivated to abuse.
2. The potential offender overcomes internal inhibitions against acting on that motivation, eg by alcohol abuse or the failure of incest inhibition mechanisms.
3. The potential offender overcomes external impediments to committing abuse, eg lack of supervision, unusual opportunities to be alone with the child and an absent mother.
4. The potential offender undermines a child's possible resistance to sexual abuse, eg unusual trust between the child and the offender, coercion.

Treatment of child sex abusers

Craissati asks: 'Are some perpetrators unsuitable for community treatment? The answer to this is probably very few...Impulsivity and compliance are the two issues to consider: If a perpetrator has demonstrated high levels of impulsivity in the past, to the extent that he appears to have very limited capacity to resist compelling urges to assault children, then he should perhaps only enter a community treatment programme if he is willing to take anti-libidinal medication.'[71] Otherwise he should be managed judicially by imprisonment, parole and probation. Craissati[73] also writes that in terms of compliance, a history of childhood sexual victimisation and a previous history of sexual or violent offending together were highly predictive of poor compliance in the treatment programme offered. She concludes:

> There are a few perpetrators whose offence history has escalated to such a degree, or contains evidence of sadism which indicates that they undoubtedly pose a high threat of very severe physical harm to children in the community.[74]

She recommends that such men do not take part in a compulsory treatment programme imposed by the Courts and monitored by the Probation Service because it does not work for this group, and would jeopardise the majority who do benefit from the programme – through loss of public confidence.

Treatment programme components for child sex abusers

- Breaking down the person's denial of the offence.
- Victim empathy is developed.
- Challenging the abuser's self justification for his actions.
- Increase self-esteem to help lower fears of adult intimacy by addressing lifestyle issues.
- Modify deviant sexual fantasies (these denote a poor prognosis).
- Relapse prevention by helping abusers recognise situations of temptation and their concomitant moods, feelings and thoughts and to develop strategies to prevent relapse.

How should the Church help in the rehabilitation of sex offenders?
This is dealt with in a publication produced by Churches Together in Britain and Ireland,[75] summarising parts of the Board of Social Responsibility of the Church of England's (1999) publication *Meeting the Challenge: How Churches Should Respond to Sex Offenders*.[76] In the introduction, the Rt Revd Richard Harries, the Bishop of Oxford, wrote, 'the instinct of Christian compassion is to be generous, but this proper spirit needs to be tempered by the risk sex offenders pose and the manipulative strategies they use'. The document lists some of the methods sex offenders often use to try and perpetrate their offences – methods that must make churches wary:

- They often minimise the extent of their offending or may deny it entirely.
- They like people to believe they are 'nice guys' and may try to impress others with the depth of their Christian commitment.
- Sex offenders use a process of 'grooming' to 'target' their victims (and may well 'groom' not only the individual potential victim, but their family and the church community).
- Sex offenders often move around from job to job and place to place, so that their activities are not easily monitored.

- Sex offenders have distorted belief systems that are very well established. Treatment programmes may help control their activities, but find it harder to change their beliefs.
- Sex offenders (especially those who have served a prison sentence) may have a conversion experience and embrace the Christian faith wholeheartedly. But it is important to understand how this new found faith is functioning. An immature faith may in fact be dysfunctional in some areas, while providing definite benefits for psychosocial integration in others. As such, an immature faith is often a way of deflecting people from the reality of their offending as well as being a way of covering up the grooming process they are operating. It can also be a way of avoiding responsibility for their offences. A mature faith can of course do the opposite, namely challenge the converted person to face up to the responsibility of who they are, and help them to try to find ways of addressing their problems in a way that recognises the distress their actions cause.
- Sex offenders come from all backgrounds, classes and professions.
- Sex offenders are known for their resistance to change. People who work with them know that effecting change is part of a long-term process.

The good practice recommended by *Meeting the Challenge* includes the following:

- liaising with diocesan and parish child protection officers (who are likely to have links with external agencies);
- maybe set up a small group to befriend and keep a careful watch on the person;
- if you are concerned about someone's inappropriate behaviour, tell someone and make sure that the person is not left alone with children and young people;
- explore what confidentiality means in this situation (so that it does not preclude sharing essential information);
- offer support to families of sex offenders, who are often 'forgotten victims'.

Additionally, if the person is a Christian, an assessment can be made of how the client or patient's religious belief is functioning. Thus, spirituality may actually be dysfunctional, a cover-up for some need for status or power, or of a more profound pathology. On the other hand, spirituality may be the door that is an opening on to a new life in which the person will be able to cope with life more effectively than before. This is very important to know. Sometimes, a patient's spirituality is both dysfunctional and helps them to cope with life more effectively than before, even at the same time that spirituality is constantly changing and developing. An instrument such as the Religious Status Inventory (RSI) or Interview, originally developed by Paul Pruyser of the Menninger Foundation in the USA and consequently developed by Malony[77] could prove valuable in this respect. As regards sexual abuse, Hall[78] has conducted research on the victims, using the RSI, and the results have proved instructive.

Christians with paedophilia should be made aware of the effects on their victims. Such Christians can then be given an opportunity to develop a genuine Christian maturity, in which self-awareness of the grooming process is made explicit and responsibility for actions is learnt. Self-awareness should also extend to the way in which their faith is functioning, so that each dimension (there are eight in the original design) can be seen for what it really is. Denial should therefore be discouraged as regards the grooming process, since it can no longer be dressed up in a religious garb.

Meeting the Challenge provides the following information sheet on how to plan the integration of known offenders:

> *Where a known offender joins a church it will be important to extend love and friendship to the individual, but at the same time the leadership will need to ensure that a frank discussion takes place with the person concerned and efforts are made to sustain open communications.*
>
> *It will be necessary to establish clear boundaries for both the protection of the young people and to lessen the possibility of the adult being wrongly accused of abuse. The following points should be addressed:*
>
> * *Church leaders should ensure they maintain close links with a probation officer (if any).*
> * *Be open with the offender.*
> * *Prepare a contract which includes:*
>   - *attending designated meetings only,*
>   - *sitting apart from children,*
>   - *staying away from areas of the building where children meet,*

- attending a house group where there are no children,
- declining hospitality where there are children,
- never being alone with children,
- never working with children.
- *Get the offender to sign the contract.*
- *Enforce the contract – do not allow them to manipulate you.*
- *Consider whether to tell the church.*
- *Ensure key leaders know the situation (if you don't tell the church).*
- *Provide close support and pastoral care.*
- *Ban the offender from church if the contract is broken and tell other churches or probation officer.*[79]

Conclusion: suggestions for ways forward

In this chapter I have attempted to define what we mean by personality disorder; why the condition is so hard to treat; and what are some of the ethical and political issues in the treatment. I have looked at the concept of psychopathy – its causes, meaning and management. Issues of moral responsibility have been discussed. The biblical view appears to be that every human being is responsible for their actions to a greater or lesser extent and that there are degrees of responsibility, depending on such factors as the amount of damage the individual may have incurred in childhood through no fault of their own. The biblical view appears to be not that those who commit crimes should not be punished but that they should not be 'written off'. Where treatment is possible it should be sought and offered.

The treatment of this group of people is ubiquitously regarded as a challenge. A Christian view, as espoused for instance by Johnson,[53] is that we should not give up on these individuals. Moreover, there is an increasing body of literature that encourages treatability. The exact degree of treatability by mental health services is not known but seems linked to factors such as: the individual; the therapist; the institutional therapeutic setting; the level of resourcing. In addition, it may be possible for the church and individual Christians to help pioneer a Christ-like approach.

Such an approach might envisage many people who are antisocial as 'weaker brethren'. They cannot cope with levels of temptation that other people manage without difficulty. If they are

Christians, their faith may well be dysfunctional, and in need of correction. Given that certain therapies may be more efficacious than was previously thought, both the culture of the therapist and of the maladjusted person need to be addressed, perhaps within the context of a therapeutic community with specific moral boundaries. Churches and professionals can work together to produce a model of community that has the potential to help these difficult-to-manage patients.

4

Responsibility and the mentally ill offender

M Dominic Beer and Janet M Parrott

Dr Beer and Dr Parrott examine whether the insane criminal is responsible for their actions.

What is the biblical view of responsibility?

How does English law view insanity and diminished responsibility? What is the insanity defence?

What are some of the psychiatric defences in English law?

How can Christian health professionals manage the psychotic offender?

Biblical perspectives on responsibility

The question of intent

The Old Testament law set out clear principles with regard to responsibility for serious offences and current law in the UK still largely mirrors this early framework. There is a particular focus in scripture on the position with regard to murder and on the perpetrator's intent at the time of committing the prohibited act. The killing is required to be intentional. This is stated in the law given to Moses by God:

> *Anyone who strikes a man and kills him shall surely be put to death. However, if he does not do it intentionally, but God lets it happen, he is to flee to a place I will designate. (Exodus 21:12–13)*

Similarly,

> *But if without hostility someone suddenly pushes another*
> *or throws something at him unintentionally or, without*
> *seeing him, drops a stone on him that could kill him, and he*
> *dies, then since he was not his enemy and he did not intend*
> *to harm him, the assembly must judge between him and the*
> *avenger of blood. (Numbers 35:22–24)*

The Old Testament law therefore recognised manslaughter where there was no intent to kill and that safe havens were available to the perpetrator. Moses set aside three cities east of the Jordan to which anyone who had killed a person could flee if he had unintentionally killed his neighbour without malice aforethought (Dt 4:41–42).

Attention is given to the manner in which a person's behaviour informs the issue of intent. 'But if a man hates his neighbour and lies in wait for him, assaults and kills him, and then flees to one of these cities, the elders of his town shall send for him, bring him back from the city, and hand him to the avenger of blood to die' (Dt 19:11). The principle of requiring such intent is reiterated later to Joshua, thus underlining its importance.

> *Then the Lord said to Joshua: 'Tell the Israelites to*
> *designate the cities of refuge, as I instructed you through*
> *Moses, so that anyone who kills a person accidentally and*
> *unintentionally may flee there and find protection from the*
> *avenger of blood'. (Joshua 20:1–3)*

Is there any biblical evidence for degrees of moral responsibility?
First, the Bible endorses the principle whereby those who have been given more understanding, gifts and talents will be more strictly judged by God.

> *Not many of you should presume to be teachers, my*
> *brothers, because you know that we who teach will be*
> *judged more strictly. (James 3:1)*

The Apostle Paul writes:

> *Now you, if you call yourself a Jew; if you rely on the*
> *law and brag about your relationship to God; if you know*
> *his will and approve of what is superior because you are*
> *instructed by the law; if you are convinced that you are a*

*guide for the blind, a light for those who are in the dark, an
instructor of the foolish, a teacher of infants, because you
have in the law the embodiment of knowledge and truth
– you, then, who teach others, do you not teach yourself?
You who preach against stealing, do you steal? You who
say that people should not commit adultery, do you commit
adultery? You who abhor idols, do you rob temples? You
who brag about the law, do you dishonour God by breaking
the law? (Romans 2:17–23)*

The principle of God's people being subject to greater accountability
and responsibility is also found in the ministry of Jesus when he
taught the parable of the wise servant waiting for his master:

*That servant who knows his master's will and does not get
ready or does not do what his master wants will be beaten
with many blows. But the one who does not know and
does things deserving punishment will be beaten with few
blows. (Luke 12:47–48)*

Jesus concludes: 'From everyone who has been given much, much
will be demanded; and from the one who has been entrusted with
much, much more will be asked' (Lk 12:48).

Second, we are all judged on what we do with the abilities
we have been given. Jesus told the parable of the talents. One man
invested his five talents so as to make five more; another invested his
two talents and made another two; the third buried his one talent in
the ground. The first two were commended:

*Well done, good and faithful servant! You have been faithful
with a few things; I will put you in charge of many things.
Come and share your master's happiness. (Matthew 25:21–23)*

The man who buried his talent was called 'you wicked, lazy servant'
(v.26) and was thrown 'outside into the darkness' (v.30).

The parable was told in the context of teaching about God's
Kingdom: 'For everyone who has will be given more, and he will
have abundance. Whoever does not have, even what he has will be
taken from him' (v.29). This speaks of eternal judgment and one of the
key points is the servant's heart attitude to the master. This eternal
and spiritual viewpoint is not necessarily completely applicable to
a secular and temporary state. Nevertheless the principle of being
judged for one's moral attitude appears to pertain in both the spiritual
and the temporal realms.

A third and allied principle is that we are judged according to the revelation of God that we have. Paul develops the theme of moral and spiritual responsibility.

> *All who sin apart from the law will also perish apart from the law, and all who sin under the law will be judged by the law. For it is not those who hear the law who are righteous in God's sight, but it is those who obey the law who will be declared righteous. (Indeed, when Gentiles, who do not have the law, do by nature things required by the law, they are a law for themselves, even though they do not have the law, since they show that the requirements of the law are written on their hearts, their consciences also bearing witness, and their thoughts now accusing, now even defending them.) This will take place on the day when God will judge men's secrets through Jesus Christ, as my gospel declares. (Romans 2:12–16)*

So, Paul writes that even those who do not have the written law will be judged by what their own consciences have recognised.

The legal position

The question of intent is central to the legal concept of responsibility in the UK and this view has its foundations in both Jewish law and Greek moral philosophy. Aristotle wrote 'it is only to (voluntary actions) that we assign praise or blame … actions are commonly regarded as involuntary when they are performed under compulsion or as a result of ignorance'. He offers an example of ignorance:

> *If a man gives his wife her medicine, and unwittingly administers poison and kills her, he is not responsible for her death.*[1]

In English law accused persons are presumed to be 'responsible' for their actions unless they can show this is untrue for any particular act. The factors considered to have a bearing on this issue are mistake, provocation, duress and insanity. For offences of strict liability, however, these factors are no defence – responsibility is always present. An example would be a vendor's liability for selling adulterated goods.

Assignment of criminal responsibility or blameworthiness usually requires two elements to be present, the *actus rea* (prohibited act) and the *mens rea* (guilty mind). The English jurist from the 13th

Century, Henri de Bracton, wrote: 'A crime is not committed unless the will to harm be present'. Mental illness continues to be viewed as excusing a person from blame and liability to punishment within certain confines which have their basis both in statute and case law. There are parallels in the way that actions are justified through particular circumstances, eg when someone acts in self defence or under provocation where it is argued that a voluntary act was necessary in the circumstances. There is an acceptance of responsibility but not of liability to moral censure. The American Model Penal Code of 1962 explicitly codifies degrees *of mens rea* as follows:

> *purposely – the actor intends a harmful outcome;*
> *knowingly – the actor knows harm is very likely but*
> *proceeds anyway; recklessly – the actor consciously*
> *disregards a substantial and unjustifiable risk and*
> *negligently – the actor is unaware, but ought to be of a*
> *substantial and unjustifiable risk. English common law*
> *makes similar distinctions.*[2]

Mental disorder and the law

Offenders with mental disorder constitute a minority of all offenders and there are considerable differences between countries in respect of definitions, attitudes, legal practice and the role of the psychiatrist. The situation in England and Wales will be described in more detail, which will illustrate more generalisable themes.

Psychiatric disorder is most usually taken into account after a finding of guilt in order to inform sentencing. The most usual sentence imposed for significant offence behaviour is the imposition of a hospital order, which results in the defendant being admitted to hospital for a period of treatment. Less serious offending can be dealt with by the use of conditional discharge or a community rehabilitation order, where the offender agrees to supervision by the probation service. Where the offence is serious and when a person is charged with murder, certain defences are available during the trial process and it is on these occasions that psychiatrists are asked to assist the court in its determination of whether a defendant is responsible.

Psychiatric defences

Automatism
The defence of automatism refers to an involuntary act, ie where there was no intent to commit the offence. If the act is considered to fall within the remit of what is referred to in law as a non-insane automatism such a finding leads to an acquittal. The law considers that the behaviour should not be considered to constitute a criminal offence, ie that no *actus rea* has occurred. An example might be an assault committed during a state of concussion following a head injury. However, if the automatism arises from an internal cause, in legal terms a 'disease of the mind' then the defence is one of insane automatism. The outcome of such a finding is likely to be detention in hospital. Epilepsy is regarded as a 'disease of the mind' in this context as the law is seen as including all those conditions due to internal factors that may be associated with violence and which may recur. The legal distinction between internal and external causes has no physical basis.

The insanity defence
The special verdict in English law of 'not guilty by reason of insanity' was first used in 1800 at the trial of James Hadfield who shot at King George III. This was further developed after the trial of Daniel McNaughton that led to the development of the McNaughton rules in 1843. Daniel McNaughton believed his life was in danger because of a plot orchestrated by the British Tory Party. He believed he was being followed by agents deployed for this purpose by the Tories. He was so plagued by these beliefs that he went to strike at the Tory Party's very head, namely the Prime Minister. He did indeed kill whom he thought was the Prime Minister, but it transpired that he had mistaken Sir Edward Drummond, the Prime Minister's Secretary, for Sir Robert Peel when he shot him in Whitehall.

In the ensuing trial it was argued successfully that McNaughton should be declared not guilty by reason of insanity and he was committed to the Bethlem Royal Hospital. Following this verdict, there was a public outcry, in no small way backed by Queen Victoria herself who had been subject to a number of assassination attempts, including one the previous year at the hands of one Edward Oxford in Hyde Park. As a result of these criticisms a debate in the House of Lords led to the formulation of the 'McNaughton Rules' as the legal test of responsibility so as to clarify when the defence could be used.

The judgment stated that:

> ...to establish a defence on the grounds of insanity, it must
> be clearly proved that at the time of committing the act, the
> party accused was labouring under such a defect of reason,
> from disease of the mind, as not to know the nature and
> quality of the act he was doing, or if he did know it, that
> he did not know that what he was doing was wrong.[3]

The insanity defence has a cognitive basis, emphasising ignorance as the exculpatory factor. The defining criterion is impaired reasoning due to 'disease of the mind', which has been amplified in case law as 'major mental illness...for which a person should be detained in hospital'.[4] A similar cognitive test of insanity based on the English McNaughton Rules applies in the legal systems within Scotland, New Zealand, Australia, Canada and many States of America. The Insanity Defence is decided by a jury 'on the balance of probabilities', as in civil litigation, rather than requiring the more stringent standard of proof beyond reasonable doubt, used in criminal proceedings. Although it applies to any offence, its use in the UK is uncommon and generally reserved for serious offences.

Diminished responsibility
The introduction of the defence of diminished responsibility in the 1957 Homicide Act introduced a volitional test in England and Wales and the idea that mental illness may lead to the defendant being partially excused from blame.

It is now the most usual defence raised to a charge of murder in defendants who are mentally disordered. Section two of the Homicide Act states that it is for the defence to raise the issue and if the defence is accepted the charge is reduced to one of manslaughter allowing wide discretion in sentencing.

The concept of diminished responsibility originated in Scotland in common law in 1867.[5] Later the Scottish judge, Lord Alness, explained[6] that some people could be considered completely responsible for their actions, some completely irresponsible and there was a middle group who:

> While they may not merit the description of being insane,
> are nevertheless in such a condition as to reduce the quality
> of their act from murder to culpable homicide. There must
> be mental unsoundness; there must be a state of mind
> bordering on though not amounting to insanity.

> *There must be a mind so affected that responsibility is
> diminished from full responsibility to partial responsibility.*

Intoxication

The Courts are reluctant to allow intoxication with alcohol or illicit
drugs as an excuse for antisocial behaviour. Intoxication can, however,
provide a defence to crimes of specific intent, such as murder, but
not to those of basic intent (eg manslaughter, rape). Intoxication
that merely makes a defendant more likely to behave as he did is
no defence. In crimes of basic intent the fact that the intoxication
was self induced provides the necessary *mens rea.*[7] If intoxication,
however, causes mental illness, such as a drug induced psychosis
or a toxic confusional state, the general defences outlined above are
available.

Clinical aspects of mental health and offending

Offence behaviour can be associated with a wide range of mental
illness but it is important to bear in mind that violent or antisocial
acts are uncommon. A willingness to support those vulnerable to
severe mental illness, to develop their potential and avoid relapse
by meeting their health, social and spiritual needs, should be
central to our community response. The small minority who have
offended in the context of mental illness require similar support,
although formal mental health services necessarily have a more
prominent role.

This group may have complex needs in relation to symptom
control, housing, work, childcare and safety to self and others.
Support and treatment from a psychiatric team may include
medication and psychological treatment and it is crucial that
friends and family have an understanding of the relevant issues,
such as relapse indicators and the use of longer-term medication
on a prophylactic basis to reduce the likelihood of a re-emergence
of symptoms.

Common forms of mental disorder

Affective disorder (depression or bipolar affective disorder)
Depressive illness varies considerably in nature and degree, from periods of intermittent low mood, with moderate impact on day to day life, to severe illness, associated with suicidal thoughts and abnormal beliefs. The sufferer feels useless, inadequate and hopeless and these feelings are much more powerful than the short episodes of unhappiness that we all experience from time to time. We say someone is significantly depressed when these feelings do not go away quickly. Loss of appetite and weight, irritability or restlessness, difficulty in getting off to sleep and early morning wakening may accompany such feelings.

The rare violent acts by those with severe depressive illness most commonly arise in situations linked with suicidal ideation. Depressive homicide most often either involves a man killing his wife or a mother her child in the context of suicidal thoughts. The killing is generally viewed by the patient as at least partly altruistic on account of thoughts that the victim would also be better off dead as the world is viewed in such a hostile manner. Fire-setting is also a possibility mediated by depressive ideation either in a similar context of suicide or through the illness releasing the usually inhibited feelings of anger that might ordinarily be repressed or verbalised. About one in ten people who suffer from serious depression also have periods when they are elated and overactive – when the illness is called bipolar affective disorder. The disinhibition and irritability of mania may also lead to aggressive behaviour, although serious violence is uncommon. Consistent drug or alcohol use, however, compounds the risk. Both types of mood disorder may be associated with shoplifting on account of poor concentration, diminished concern about social rules or other emotional factors.

Case history 1: depressive homicide

A 65 year old quiet and kindly man became depressed following retirement with prominent worrying preoccupations about his wife's previous affair and her increasing dependence on him. He felt worthless and desperately hopeless with regard to the future. When his wife asked him to make some effort to get some shopping he experienced the sudden thought that if he killed her and

*himself this would release his wife from his burdensome
presence and put an end to his fears for the future. He
strangled her and took an overdose of antidepressants. He
survived and was admitted to hospital and later pleaded
guilty to manslaughter on the grounds of diminished
responsibility. He was treated successfully with medication
and psychotherapy in a medium secure unit.*

Case history 2: deviant behaviour during a minor depressive episode

*A 45 year old male head teacher was charged with fraud.
The implementation of formal audit procedures at a church
school had led to the discovery that the head teacher had
been adding pupils to the roll prior to their official starting
date, resulting in greater financial support for the school
from the Local Authority. The head was unable to offer
an explanation, suggesting he had misinterpreted the
regulations. His wife, however, confirmed he had become
quite depressed over the previous year following some
minor criticisms arising from a school inspection. He
had become constantly anxious with disturbed sleep and
appetite and had taken to drinking more than usual on
his return from school in order to calm himself. His mood
disturbance responded to treatment with antidepressant
medication and through a period of supportive
psychotherapy he was able to recognise his anger and
humiliation on being criticised when under pressure.
He came to acknowledge that his submitting fraudulent
returns reflected his feelings in this area and drew some
parallels with his earlier experiences during childhood.
With appropriate support he was able to resume teaching
responsibilities and take a balanced view of his resignation
from his management position.*

Schizophrenia

Schizophrenia is a severe mental illness where contact with reality is
impaired and subjects commonly experience abnormal perceptions,
such as voices talking about them, and develop delusional beliefs,
often of a paranoid nature. Paranoid thinking can form the basis of

motivation for both violent offences and fire-setting associated with schizophrenia and similar psychotic illness.

Violent offences and fire-setting associated with schizophrenia may emanate from acting on the instructions of hallucinatory voices or in response to paranoid beliefs, the subject feeling driven to act against perceived enemies. More generalised arousal and fear can lead to loss of self control.

Violent threats by psychotic patients must be taken seriously especially in those with a history of serious violence or where there is an identifiable victim.

Communication with relevant professionals is important and most serious violence occurs in those already known to psychiatrists. Contact with a possibly violent, psychotic acquaintance in a church setting places others in a difficult position but it is usually wise to err on the side of communicating concerns in the interests of all concerned. When a patient has been able to share details of a previous illness it may be possible to agree a course of action for carers, supported by the patient, in the event of further breakdown.

Case history 3

A 35 year old female African care assistant was charged with murder of her two year old child. She had been left by her partner shortly before her child's birth. She was tearful at times and seemed to retain the hope that he would return. Friends from her local church started to notice that she seemed secretive, overly preoccupied with an inner world, and appeared to spend a lot of time praying, although it was only in retrospect they fully realised her behaviour had been quite strange.

She began to comment on the specialness of her child and neighbours noticed she was talking loudly late at night, although no-one was visiting. Her friends were shocked to hear that she had stabbed the child to death and run out into the street shouting that she was now free. When visited in prison she sat on the floor of the cell with a blanket over her and refused to engage in conversation saying she had done nothing wrong and was communing with God. On admission to a medium secure hospital she gave an account of giving birth to a child of royal blood and having to sacrifice him to save the world. She received treatment with anti-psychotic medication and gradually settled in terms of overt symptoms. The painful realisation of her behaviour towards her child occurred over a longer time period. She rarely alluded to it, save in the most indirect manner but was able to reflect on her breakdown and vulnerability in this respect.

A Christian therapeutic

The well-known World Health Organization's definition of health is a state of complete physical, mental and social well-being. The Christian would add 'spiritual' to this definition. Healing of the sick was a prominent focus of Jesus' work and Jesus came, in part at least, to heal the sick physically, mentally and spiritually. It is one of the roles of the church to continue that ministry. Jesus did not judge such individuals but sought their healing. The case of Legion offers some helpful insights (Lk 8:26–39). Legion wandered naked about the tombs shouting and harming himself. He was so violent that people feared to come near him and he had been bound by chains. Jesus did not condemn him for his violence but had compassion and after being set free by Jesus the man returned to 'his right mind'.

From the perspective of promoting mental health, both the absence of mental illness and the capacity to function in a mutual, responsible manner within a community are important. Freud summarised this capacity as 'the ability to love and to work'. It is at the core of Christian belief that we live in a disordered world in need of restoration both at an individual and societal level.

When illness has been associated with offending, both victims and perpetrators need a response from a community that is creative of new possibilities, a restorative justice.[8] An acknowledgement of wrong is intrinsic to forgiveness but in this context supporting the perpetrator in taking responsibility for his health needs to be our main concern.

What is our role as Christian health professionals?

In view of Jesus' treatment of the above example, perhaps we can employ the following rules of thumb:

- We are to heal the sick as Jesus did.
- We are not to judge or condemn.

- We are to consider the very sick person as not 'in their right mind'.
- We are not to hold the very sick person as being responsible for their actions.

Conclusion

The response of society through the English legal system may incorporate both punishment and treatment. An imposition of compulsory detention and treatment contains both elements and similarly combines the dual necessity of both the individual and the community through the Health Service taking responsibility to minimise future risk. Ministry to the sick has been part of the church's role from the earliest times and Christian health professionals can reflect on the great privilege of being able to work in this area. Rowan Clare Williams[9] reminds us that our defined roles protect us from the torrent of pain that is most people's story and cautions us to be wary of our professionalism becoming an excuse that avoids identifying with the people we deal with. Our awareness of our own vulnerability and need of God's forgiving love supports a compassionate but realistic view of offending associated with mental illness.

5

Treatments used in psychiatry and Christian counselling

M Dominic Beer

> This chapter provides a brief review of the more usual approaches to physical, psychological, social and spiritual treatments of the mentally ill person.
>
> What are the biological treatments used in psychiatry? How effective is medication and electroconvulsive therapy?
>
> What are the common psychological treatments used in psychiatry?
> Are these to be used for Christians?
>
> What is the nature of Christian counselling and specific prayer ministry for Christians?
>
> The chapter concludes with a series of vignettes that might occur in the daily work of a practitioner, which will be of help not only to specialists in their respective fields, but also to pastoral workers who would like insight into treatments that are outside their normal remit.

Physical treatments

1. Antidepressant medication

Antidepressants are drugs that affect neurotransmission in the brain. As their primary mode of action they affect the neurotransmitters called serotonin and noradrenaline. The drugs may take up to two weeks to take effect and up to six weeks for full effect. The two main categories of commonly used drugs are selective serotonin reuptake inhibitors (SSRIs), which block the reuptake mainly of serotonin, thus leaving more available at the nerve ending of the brain cell, and tricyclic antidepressants (TCAs), which block the reuptake of serotonin and also of noradrenaline. The SSRI most commonly prescribed is Prozac (fluoxetine). The side-effects of SSRIs are mainly gastrointestinal (nausea and diarrhoea) and headache. The side-effects of the TCAs include dry mouth, sedation, low blood pressure on standing, visual problems and constipation, which are at least partly because they affect the autonomic nervous system controlling 'automatic' functions. The TCAs also have cardiac effects and can be fatal in overdose. The SSRIs are very rarely fatal in overdose. Some of the latter, eg fluoxetine, tend to be effective antidepressants at the starting dose, whereas the TCAs need to be increased in dose.

About 60–70% of patients respond to the first antidepressant. A further 10–15% respond to the second drug or to electroconvulsive therapy (ECT). It is important that the patient completes the course of treatment, which will be for at least six months after recovery from the episode of depression. Antidepressants are not addictive but it is still important to reduce them slowly because a 'discontinuation syndrome' can occur (patients may experience flu-like symptoms, insomnia, irritability or other symptoms).

2. Mood stabilising drugs

These are for bipolar affective disorder (which includes episodes of elevated mood, known as mania, and depression). The most well known drug is:

(a) Lithium. Lithium is a metal in the same 'chemical family' as sodium and potassium, which are essential minerals in body cells. It can be used as a treatment for mania but its main use is to prevent episodes of mania and depression, usually in those who have already had at least two episodes. Blood monitoring has to take place because there is a risk of thyroid and kidney damage and because there is only a relatively small gap between the therapeutic dose and the toxic dose.

Care has to be taken because the levels of lithium are also increased when the patient is dehydrated, has diarrhoea, or other drugs are taken, like non-steroidal anti-inflammatory drugs or diuretics (thiazides). Other side-effects include shaking and worsening of skin conditions.

(b) Sodium valproate. This is becoming increasingly popular as a mood stabiliser, because for some patients it is as effective as lithium and for others is more effective than lithium for so-called rapid cycling bipolar conditions. However, blood levels should still be taken especially in the first six months and blood tests taken to exclude liver damage and blood problems. Weight gain and gastrointestinal side-effects can also be problems. However, it has a wider therapeutic window than lithium, ie the gap between a therapeutic and a toxic level is larger. Because of adverse effects on the fetus it appears that new guidelines may advise against its use in women of childbearing age.

(c) Carbamazepine. Like sodium valproate this is also an anticonvulsant (anti-epileptic drug) and its chemical structure is similar to the TCAs. It requires blood monitoring because of potential liver damage and blood problems. Other side-effects include rash, dizziness, drowsiness, unsteadiness and nausea. It interacts with many commonly used drugs which increase its levels in the blood.

3. Antipsychotic medication ('major tranquillisers')

These are the drugs that are used effectively in the treatment of schizophrenia. Research has also shown that they reduce the rate of relapse in those with established schizophrenia. They may take up to two weeks to take effect. They are also known as major tranquillisers or neuroleptics. The name 'tranquilliser' needs explanation. It does not mean sedation, though sedation is a recognised side-effect of some of these drugs. Tranquillisation has the sense here of 'making tranquil', calm, a 'mind at peace'. The mind of the schizophrenic patient is often not at peace, but the patient is tormented by imaginary persecutors and voices of non-existent people. This is due to brain dysfunction: under neuroimaging there is a visible disturbance in certain areas of the brain when the patient is hallucinating (including the temporal region). These drugs were discovered by accident in the 1950s. They block the receptors in the brain where dopamine is active because in such patients there is an excess of this chemical in certain parts of the brain. Although they have helped many patients with schizophrenia, they remain unpopular with some people because of their side-effects and because in some people they do not help the symptoms. They are not curative but, in the three quarters of patients who have more than one episode of schizophrenia, they are necessary to prevent relapse.

These drugs typically have the following side-effects: movement disorders – spasms (in ten percent), shaking (in 20%), restlessness (in 20%) and long-term abnormal involuntary movements (in about 20%); dry mouth, blurred vision and constipation (anti-cholinergic effects); low blood pressure on standing; sex hormone effects (too much of the hormone prolactin in the blood giving rise to cessation of periods or breast growth in men); risk of epileptic seizures; body over-heating due to muscle spasm (neuromuscular malignant syndrome in one percent and which is potentially fatal); weight gain (seven percent increase in a quarter of patients).

All the antipsychotics have the same effectiveness, with the exception of clozapine which has been shown to be effective in two thirds of patients who do not respond to other antipsychotics. Regular blood taking is required to ensure that the white blood cells (which fight infection) are healthy (clozapine causes a reduction in three percent of patients). The drugs do not have the same side-effects. The main adverse effects of older antipsychotics are movement disorders, whereas the newer ones tend to affect the sex hormones and cause more weight gain. Some of the drugs can also be given in a long acting form, eg a depot injection whereby the drug is released gradually over some weeks.

4. Benzodiazepines

These drugs (such as diazepam) have a number of uses:

(a) Anti-anxiety effects. These are particularly useful when a person has depression and anxiety together and the benzodiazepine can be used in the first few days or weeks before the antidepressant takes effect.

(b) Hypnotic effect. To help with insomnia.

(c) Sedative effect. In the treatment of disturbed behaviour, usually in conjunction with an antipsychotic drug.

The main problem with this category of drugs is that they are addictive – the body becomes tolerant to their effects and increasingly larger doses have to be used for the same effect. The patient becomes dependent and suffers withdrawal symptoms if they are stopped. Consequently they should generally only be used for a period of a few weeks.

5. Cholinesterase inhibitors – antidementia drugs

These drugs are used in the treatment of senile dementia (of the Alzheimer type). They block the breakdown of the brain transmitter acetylcholine which declines in Alzheimer's. Over a six-month period a third of patients improve and a further third fail to deteriorate. Longer term, it appears that improvement rates decrease.

6. Electroconvulsive therapy (ECT)

This is a controversial but effective treatment in psychiatry whereby a grand mal seizure is induced after a small electric current is passed across the brain. When it was introduced in the 1930s and 1940s many severely depressed patients were successfully treated and subsequently discharged after many years in hospital. It received a bad name after adverse publicity, eg its portrayal in the film *One Flew over the Cuckoo's Nest*. Here it was abused as a punishment for antisocial, violent behaviour. It is an effective, safe treatment for severe depression but may also be used for mania and rarely for acute schizophrenia. In former times it was used without muscle relaxant or general anaesthetic and some patients received injuries during the seizure. Nowadays such injuries do not occur because the patient is briefly unconscious and there is full muscle relaxation. Patients may have a headache afterwards. At least one-third of patients report significant memory loss after treatment. Rose *et al*[1] in a systematic review of memory loss conclude that patients complain of long-term memory deficits, especially of autobiographical memory (retrograde memory). The ability to form new memories (anterograde memory) does not appear to be impaired. Both the National Institute of Clinical Excellence (2003)[2] and the Royal College of Psychiatrists (1990)[3] state that further research regarding long-term memory deficits is needed. The full mode of action of ECT is not known. ECT is used particularly in elderly patients who are depressed, not eating, suicidal or deluded and who cannot tolerate medication because of the side-effects (such as low blood pressure which may lead to falls and broken bones).

Psychotherapies

> *The Sovereign Lord has given me an instructed tongue, to know the word that sustains the weary. (Isaiah 50:4)*

The guiding objective of all the psychotherapies is to provide treatment using psychological means which usually involves talking. For a detailed critique from a Christian angle, see Hurding[4] and for a briefer overview see Land.[5] There are a number of talking therapies.

1. Cognitive behavioural psychotherapy

Behaviour is influenced by people's cognitions, by the way that people think – hence the term cognitive behavioural psychotherapy. Cognitive therapy is one where faulty thinking is being addressed. The Bible endorses this cognitive approach: King David wrote in the Psalms 'Why are you downcast, O my soul…?' (Ps 42:5). Later in the Psalm, he writes 'I will yet praise him'. Paul in Romans 12:1,2 urges us '…to offer [our] bodies as living sacrifices – this is your spiritual act of worship. Do not conform any longer to the pattern of this world, but be transformed by the renewing of your mind'. He also urges us to have the 'mind of Christ' (1 Cor 2.16). 'Finally, brothers, whatever is true, whatever is noble, whatever is right, whatever is pure, whatever is lovely, whatever is admirable – if anything is excellent or praiseworthy – think about such things' (Phil 4:8). Thus as Christians the way that we think is seen as important spiritually and worthy of 'renewal'. Cognitive therapy addresses wrong thought patterns. An example of a wrong thought could be 'everything I do is useless'. In cognitive therapy, the therapist challenges these thought patterns and helps the person think more positively about themselves and their situation. For the Christian it is helpful to use biblically based concepts, eg 'my value is based on my value to God'; 'he created me and loved me so much that he sent Jesus to die for my sins'; 'God gave me certain gifts and abilities that he wants me to use for him, for others and for myself'.

Cognitive therapy is an effective treatment for depression. In anxiety conditions and phobias it is combined with cognitive behavioural therapy (CBT), eg using the principles of exposure whereby the patient is exposed to the feared situation in a graded and manageable way. CBT is also used to treat obsessive–compulsive disorder where patients have intrusive thoughts and perform rituals such as checking locks, hand-washing etc.

The Behavioural School of Psychotherapy, which stresses learned behaviour, was originally demonstrated by the Russian physiologist Ivan Pavlov with his dog experiments. Dogs were fed after a bell sounded but Pavlov was able to condition them to prepare for their meal – by salivation after the bell – even when the meal was not forthcoming. Joseph Wolpe, J. B. Watson and B. F. Skinner pursued this in human beings with concepts such as 'positive reinforcement' – where a behaviour is reinforced by its consequences – and 'extinction' where a behaviour diminishes in frequency. The principles underlying this approach are used in treatment of phobias. The behaviourist approach taken to its extremes has little room for the Christian viewpoint because it does not allow for the spiritual side of human beings.

Although these therapies are associated with Freud, this is a simplification. Firstly, talking therapy between the doctor (or another person doing the treatment) and the patient, has been part of treatment for hundreds of years. Richard Baxter wrote in 1716: 'A great part of their cure lieth in pleasing them...interrupt their musings; raise them out of it but with loving importunity'.[6] 'Moral treatment' was made famous at 'The Retreat', the Quaker mental hospital in the late eighteenth/early nineteenth centuries. Although it was infused with Christian principles this was not its only emphasis. 'Moral' here had the connotation of psychological, behavioural and occupational. It was at the end of the nineteenth century that Freud provided a type of therapy which developed the theory of the patient and therapist or analyst. He believed that it was the 'analyst's' role to challenge the 'psychological defences' that the patient was employing in order to avoid dealing with impulses. Freud emphasised the sexual side of our nature and in so doing his version of psychotherapy (classical psychoanalysis) can be viewed as too one-sided from a Christian point of view. His colleague, then rival, Carl Gustav Jung, was the son of a Christian pastor. Unlike Freud he emphasised the role of the spiritual in man. However, this was not a specifically Christian approach. Rather, he incorporated mystical and Hindu concepts. As such he has been rightly criticised for not distinguishing sufficiently between good and evil (eg by Leanne Payne).

There are many other schools of psychotherapy and the most important element to most of them is the therapist–patient relationship. The interpersonal therapies differ in this respect from cognitive behavioural psychotherapy, where there is more emphasis on rating scales, measurement of symptoms, etc.

Classical psychoanalytic psychotherapy is based on three premises:

1. That much of human behaviour is driven by unconscious processes which obey different rules from the conscious mind. These unconscious processes are determined by

unacceptable sexual and aggressive impulses. Freud called these unconscious processes the 'id'.

2. The 'ego' is that part of the personality which deals with the outside world and which embodies conscious thought. The ego uses defences to avoid becoming aware of these unconscious processes. Denial is one such defence, which is a refusal consciously to recognise external reality. Depression is the basic ego defence mechanism, which is a refusal to recognise internal reality. This leads to a prevention of perceiving feelings and an unconscious inhibition of the impulse that is leading to a conflict in the individual.

3. Patients in therapy will transfer on to their therapist, feelings, relationships and environments derived from their childhood. This is called 'repetition compulsion'. It is claimed that here all of us tend unconsciously to repeat old patterns of relating from traumatic or 'stuck' relationships from the past. These relationships are called 'transference relationships'. The patient interacts with the therapist in a similar way to how he has interacted with important figures in his life (father, mother, parental figure). The therapist, at the right time and in the right way, feeds back ('interprets') to the patient what the patient is doing. This is a very skilled process requiring training to know what, how and when to interpret. Indeed most therapies insist that their therapists undergo a period of therapy themselves in order to understand these issues more fully.

An example of interpretations may be if the patient gets angry with the therapist for going on holiday, the latter might interpret that as 'you couldn't get your way, ie to see me these next two weeks. This is how you reacted when you could not get your way with your mother. Now you are doing the same with your wife at home, and with me in therapy'. In this way the patient is enabled to understand why they are behaving in this way and, with understanding, to change their thinking, emotions and behaviour.

The *neo-Freudian school* emphasised social factors as well as those that Freud had. Alfred Adler, Karen Horney, Erich Fromm and Harry Stack Sullivan held that the 'here and now' were as important as past influences.

The *reality therapy school* (William Glasser, Orval Mowrer and Carl Rogers) emphasises 'doing right', facing reality and being responsible. The therapy again focuses on the present rather than the past. They say that people seeking treatment lack two basic needs in life – love and self-worth. They do not allow the patients to try to excuse their behaviour because of unconscious conflicts. Furthermore they attempt to distinguish between right and wrong. Some aspects of this form of therapy are in accordance with Christian principles, although its definition of morality is relative.

Transactional analysis (TA) (Eric Berne) is another school which states that we relate to others on one of three levels – parent, adult and child. Berne provides an exposé of the manipulative tricks that people play on each other, which is useful in understanding the way people relate inappropriately. It emphasises that the way we think and our willpower are very important elements to effect change.

The *humanistic school* emphasises 'self actualisation', for instance using Maslow's hierarchy. Maslow proposed that human beings had a hierarchy of needs: biological and physiological; safety; belongingness and love; esteem; self actualisation. This may be helpful but it would be important to acknowledge that the Christian viewpoint is excluded from what in some respects is a very constructive approach. Generally it would accord with the biblical principle of using your talents and gifts to the full.

Group psychotherapy

The same principles that are employed in interpersonal psychotherapy are used in group therapy (except that, in addition, the group itself acts as therapist). There are usually two therapists and say six to eight patients. It was found that group psychotherapy was effective in the Second World War for Armed Forces personnel suffering psychological problems. Later the Henderson Hospital opened in London for patients with personality disorders. This has been called a Therapeutic Community and the model has been repeated due to its success. There is, for instance, a Christian Therapeutic Community in Deal, UK (Community, Therapy and Rehabilitation). As can be imagined, sometimes a group of people, especially if its members have similar problems, can have a powerful effect on a patient, possibly even more potent than the views of a therapist.

Family therapy

This is a very useful treatment for children and adolescents whereby the whole family can be involved in the treatment. It is frowned upon by classical psychoanalysts who would prefer personal child psychoanalysis as practised by Anna Freud. The advantage of family therapy is that the individual is not scapegoated or seen as 'the problem'. The issues are seen in context and all protagonists given the opportunity to contribute, reflect and change. The individual is thus seen as part of a system.

Christian counselling

This could be defined as the ministry of one individual seeking to help another individual recognise, understand and solve their problems in accordance with the word of God. This section on Christian counselling has been based on Minirth and Byrd.[7] The following principles apply in Christian counselling:

1. The Bible is the final standard of authority. As a result, Christians are not left to wade through many philosophies using their own logic to try to find a correct way through. Nor do they depend on their own consciences to direct their behaviour. Some will have too sensitive a conscience, eg those who have obsessive–compulsive disorder and depression. Others will have the opposite type of conscience until it comes under the light of God's word, the Holy Spirit and other people. The Bible gives a foundation and framework. It gives insight into human behaviour, tells us what our purpose is, where we came from and what our nature is.

2. Christian counselling recognises that there is a *battle* going on between the good law in the mind waging war against the evil law in its members (Rom 7).

3. Christian counselling is unique because it does not depend only on human willpower but also on the power of the Holy Spirit to help overcome problems.

4. Christian counselling can address issues such as guilt from the *past* as well as those of the *present*, unlike other schools which emphasise one or other. The importance of *looking back* is shown by a passage such as 'If we confess our sins, he is faithful and just and will forgive us our sins and purify us from all unrighteousness' (1 Jn 1:9). The importance of *the present* is emphasised in a passage such as: '…one thing I do; Forgetting what is behind and straining towards what is ahead, I press on…' (Phil 3:13–14). NB with some people care must be taken not to make them feel inappropriate guilt, eg in obsessive–compulsive disorder, depression and during certain phases of borderline personality disorders.

5. The motivation for counselling is based on love. Because God loves us, this love flows through us, we love others and feel a responsibility to them: 'everyone who loves the father loves his child as well' (1 Jn 5:1).
6. Christian counselling can be employed across cultures, although it requires application appropriate to each culture.
7. Christian counselling seeks to deal with the *whole person*. Jesus dealt with the whole person in the healing of the invalid at the pool of Bethesda (Jn 5:1–15).

Hurding[4] lists the aims of Christian counselling as:

1. Repentance – hearing 'God's call to a radical change of direction' (p.395).
2. Restoration and reconciliation to God and to each other.
3. Redemption leading to 'releasing, rescuing and saving those in bondage…the beginnings of victory over some besetting sin, release from an obsessive habit or deliverance from an evil influence' (p.398).
4. Regeneration and sanctification by God's Holy Spirit.

Aspects of Christian counselling

And we urge you, brothers, warn those who are idle, encourage the timid, help the weak, be patient with everyone. (1 Thessalonians 5:14)

1. 'Urge' (Greek *parakleo*) meaning 'to exhort'. It is also used in Romans 12:1, 2 Corinthians 1:4 and Romans 15:30. Hurding[4] calls this the 'pastoral' role.
2. 'Warn those' (Greek *noutheteo*) (or 'admonish' in some translations) is stronger, meaning 'to warn, confront'. It is intended to produce a change in lifestyle. It is also used in Romans 15:14, 1 Corinthians 4:14 and Colossians 3:16. Hurding[4] calls this the 'prophetic' role.
3. 'Encourage' (Greek *parmutheomai*) means 'to cheer up', have a 'positive attitude'. It is also used in 1 Thessalonians 2:11. Hurding[4] calls this the 'comforter' role.
4. 'Help' (Greek *antechomai*) means 'to take an interest in', 'to be available for'.
5. 'Be patient' (Greek *makrothumeo*) means 'to have persistence'. It is also used in Matthew 18:26, 29; James 5:7 and Hebrews 6:15.

Again the ministry of Jesus shows times when he was directive and confrontational, eg the rich young ruler (Mt 19:21–23); times when he was less directive, eg when he used parables (Mt 13:3); and times when he emphasised the past and the present, eg the Samaritan woman in John 4.

The Christian counsellor

Minirth and Byrd[7] enumerate five characteristics of a wise counsellor from the book of Proverbs:

1. The counsellor is in pursuit of God. 'Instruct a wise man and he will be wiser still; teach a righteous man and he will add to his learning' (Pr 9:9). 'The fear of the Lord is the beginning of wisdom' (Ps 111:10). The Apostle Paul wrote: 'I consider everything a loss compared to the surpassing greatness of knowing Christ Jesus my Lord, for whose sake I have lost all things' (Phil 3:8). Jesus says that God seeks true worshippers, who worship him in spirit and in truth (Jn 4:23–24).

2. The counsellor has a growing understanding of God's word. 'My son, do not forget my teaching, but keep my commands in your heart, for they will prolong your life many years and bring you prosperity' (Pr 3:1–2). The word of God instructs us (Ps 119:9–11) and corrects us (1 Tim 3:16). It helps us distinguish between the issues of the mind and those of the spirit (Heb 4:12). It builds us up (Acts 20:32) and nourishes us, gives us life (Jn 6:63).

3. The counsellor understands the power of prayer. God delights in our prayers (Pr 15:8). Prayer consists of: (a) praise (Ps 9:11), (b) confession (1 Jn 1:9), which relieves us of guilt, (c) thanksgiving (Phil 4:6) which gives us encouragement and guards against bitterness, and (d) intercession (Phil 4:6).

4. The counsellor has fellowship with godly people. 'He who walks with the wise grows wise, but a companion of fools suffers harm' (Pr 13:20). 'As iron sharpens iron, so one man sharpens another' (Pr 27:17).

5. The counsellor witnesses for Christ. A truthful witness gives honest testimony (Pr 12:17a). The tongue of the wise brings healing (Pr 12:18b). Truthful lips endure forever (Pr 12:19a).

How to counsel using Jesus' example

(a) He had perfect insight into people's problems.
(b) He was an expert at asking questions – to help others gain insight, to rebuke, to teach.
(c) He cared for those he counselled.
(d) He could counsel others because of his close relationship to God the Father and his word. He knew himself.
(e) He understood what people needed to do to change.
(f) He knew when to confront and when to ask questions.

How not to counsel

Minirth and Byrd[7] point out that Job's three counsellors, Eliphaz, Bildad and Zophar, made many mistakes in their counselling:

(a) They were talkers not listeners. They were too directive and dogmatic.
(b) They failed to convey an attitude of understanding but accused in a harsh way.
(c) They were full of themselves, their own ideas and importance.
(d) They failed to see the grace and glory of God but saw God as being petty in his relations with human beings. God said to Eliphaz: 'I am angry with you and your two friends, because you have not spoken of me what is right, as my servant Job has' (Jb 42:7).

The qualities of a Christian counsellor

(a) To have an accepting attitude.
(b) To be a good listener.
(c) To know when to confront and when to suggest.
(d) To know when to bring in God's word.
(e) To know when to be matter of fact and when to be kind.
(f) To have a life purpose given over to Christ.
(g) To be personal, genuine and warm.
(h) To be unshockable. Jesus 'knew what was in a man' (Jn 2:25) and woman (Jn 4).
(i) To be confident that God can help the person.
(j) To have a sense of humour.

Therapeutic steps in Christian counselling

(a) Be kind (Pr 19:22) and gentle (1 Thes 2:7). Genuinely care, as Paul did (Rom 1:11–12; Gal 4:19).

(b) Be a good listener, use open ended questions, let the person 'ventilate'.

(c) Help the person gain insight into what the issue or problem is. 'Search me, O God, and know my heart; test me and know my anxious thoughts. See if there is any offensive way in me…' (Ps 139:23–24). It is much better that the person finds out for themselves what the issues are and finds a possible way forward. They are much more likely to agree with it, put it into practice and remember it.

(d) Help with the resolution of feelings. If anger or bitterness have arisen they need to be dealt with (Eph 4:26). The past is important, but the present is more so.

(e) Help to correct wrong thinking. Guide the person towards developing a more balanced self-concept. Emphasise taking responsibility.

(f) Develop an action plan. People have more control over their behaviour, what they do, than how they feel usually. The feelings may well follow after correct behaviour and thinking. It is helpful to have daily quiet times, physical exercise, daily social contact and avoidance of specific sins and situations where temptation may be great.

(g) Remember the physical, psychological, social and spiritual – and how they interact.

(h) Assist the person with scriptural insights, encouragements and observations towards a deeper relationship with Christ, an acceptance of themselves, their gifts as given by God and of their relationship with others and their effect on others.

Christian counselling compared with secular psychotherapy

Psychoanalysis emphasises the three parts: the 'id', the 'ego' and the 'superego'. The 'id' represents the basic drives, eg for sex and food. The 'superego' is the conscience. The 'ego' acts as the logical decision maker, refereeing between the id and the superego. Another psychotherapy, 'transactional analysis', teaches that there are the 'parent', 'adult' and 'child' components. The 'child' emphasises the feelings; the 'parent' judges and the 'adult' acts logically in a rational manner.

The Bible (Rom 7) describes the flesh, the conscience and the soul. These roughly correspond to the id/superego/ego and child/parent/adult terms, respectively. However, the Christian view adds another dimension altogether – the spiritual. Both in the New and the Old Testaments the spirit is seen as the third part along with the body and the soul. In Hebrew, *basar* loosely means body; *neshamah* means the human spirit; and *nephesh* means soul. 'May your whole spirit, soul and body be kept blameless at the coming of our Lord Jesus Christ' (1 Thes 5:23) . Some theologians propose a division into body and soul but this is an ongoing debate.

The Greek for soul is *psyche* and the author of the letter to the Hebrews again refers to the distinction between soul and spirit (Heb 4:12). Often *psyche* is translated as 'self'. Matthew 16:26 and Luke 9:25 have very similar wording but the passage uses the word soul (the other self or the person).

The Bible focuses on three functions of the soul: *the will,* Job 7:15; 6:7, where reference is made to the ability of the soul to choose; *the mind,* Proverbs 19:2, Psalm 139:4, where reference is made to the intellectual or knowing aspect of the soul; and *the emotions,* Song of Solomon 1:7.

Why may Christians have emotional problems?

Christians, like others, have been and are subject to the effects of a fallen world. The mind has been subject to many influences – physical, social and psychological, some positive, some not. Some may cause guilt, anxiety and distress. Some can be helped by means of spiritual disciplines, eg prayer, the word of God and fellowship.

The spiritual side of human beings

This is the supernatural part of man given by God at birth, not to be confused with the Holy Spirit who is given at conversion. The spirit is that part of man which communes with God: 'Yet a time is coming and has now come when the true worshippers will worship the Father in spirit and truth, for they are the kind of worshippers the Father seeks' (Jn 4:23). Becoming a Christian necessitates asking Jesus in by his Spirit – 'no-one can enter the Kingdom of God unless he is born of water and the Spirit' (Jn 3:5). Other spirits can however regrettably also be invited in, such as in the practice of witchcraft (Gal 5:20).

The Spirit is at war with the sinful side of man, called the flesh (Greek *sarx*) in the New Testament. 'For the sinful nature [flesh] desires what is contrary to the Spirit, and the Spirit what is contrary to the sinful nature. They are in conflict with each other.' (Gal 5:17)

> *I do not understand what I do. For what I want to do I do*
> *not do, but what I hate I do. And if I do what I do not want*
> *to do, I agree that the law is good. As it is, it is no longer*
> *I myself who do it, but it is sin living in me. I know that*
> *nothing good lives in me, that is, in my sinful nature. For*
> *I have the desire to do what is good, but I cannot carry it*
> *out. For what I do is not the good I want to do; no, the evil*
> *I do not want to do – this I keep on doing. Now if I do what*
> *I do not want to do, it is no longer I who do it, but it is sin*
> *living in me that does it. So I find this law at work: When*
> *I want to do good, evil is right there with me. For in my*
> *inner being I delight in God's law; but I see another law at*
> *work in the members of my body, waging war against the*
> *law of my mind and making me a prisoner of the law of sin*
> *at work within my members. What a wretched man I am!'*
> *(Romans 7:15–24a).*

Paul here shows how the 'body' is subject to sin; his 'inner being' delights in God's law; and the battleground is the 'law of my mind'.

'Who will rescue me from this body of death?' he asks (Rom 7:24b). This can only be done 'through Jesus Christ our Lord' (Rom 7:25). By God's grace we can have a fresh start and have the power to continue to live by grace with a clean conscience: 'Therefore, there is now no condemnation for those who are in Christ Jesus, because through Christ Jesus the law of the Spirit of Life set me free from the law of sin and death' (Rom 8:1–2).

Specific prayer ministry

This kind of ministry – along with inner healing, healing of the memories – are approaches that 'seek to bring the power of the risen Lord to heal and transform the hidden hurts of the past and their baleful influence on the present'.[8] What is inner healing?

> *The assumption here is that our past is an open book to*
> *God, a book in which the pages can be turned back with a*
> *sense of Christ's companionship, revealing those blotted*
> *paragraphs we had forgotten about, the pictures of which*
> *we are ashamed, the leaves that have stuck together through*
> *life's spillages. Inner healing may involve our personal*

*repentance as our hidden resentments and jealousies are
exposed, our need to forgive another as we see anew that
we have been victims and, overall, our Lord's healing of
sad, disappointing and fearful memories. The book can be
restored, its whole story knows the refreshment of the Spirit
and so becomes a clearer, less compromised tale to be told to
the glory of its divine author.*[9]

Facing the sinful side of our nature, naming it as such and engaging in a spiritual battle to deal with that nature is a specifically Christian approach to treatment and healing. This is one of the great themes of Romans 7 and 8.

*Those who live according to the sinful nature have their
minds set on what that nature desires; but those who live in
accordance with the Spirit have their minds set on what the
Spirit desires. The mind of sinful man is death, but the mind
controlled by the Spirit is life and peace; the sinful mind is
hostile to God. It does not submit to God's law, nor can it do
so. Those controlled by the sinful nature cannot please God.*

*You, however, are controlled not by the sinful nature but by
the Spirit, if the Spirit of God lives in you. And if anyone
does not have the Spirit of Christ, he does not belong to
Christ. But if Christ is in you, your body is dead because of
sin, yet your spirit is alive because of righteousness. And if
the Spirit of him who raised Jesus from the dead is living in
you, he who raised Christ from the dead will also give life to
your mortal bodies through his Spirit, who lives in you.*

*Therefore, brothers, we have an obligation—but it is not to the
sinful nature, to live according to it. For if you live according
to the sinful nature, you will die; but if by the Spirit you put
to death the misdeeds of the body, you will live, because those
who are led by the Spirit of God are sons of God. For you did
not receive a spirit that makes you a slave again to fear, but
you received the Spirit of sonship. And by him we cry, 'Abba,
Father.' The Spirit himself testifies with our spirit that we are
God's children. (Romans 8:5–16).*

The battle every believer must engage in is probably even more difficult for those with more pronounced mental health problems.

However, all of creation has been affected by the fall of man and the human mind is no exception. The mind needs to be renewed. It needs to be 'set on what the spirit desires' (Rom 8:5) rather than on 'what the sinful nature desires'. It is by the spirit that we cry 'Abba, Father'. This is a spiritual experience and not just one involving the mind:

> *In the same way, the Spirit helps us in our weakness.*
> *We do not know what we ought to pray for, but the Spirit*
> *himself intercedes for us with groans that words cannot*
> *express. And he who searches our hearts knows the mind*
> *of the Spirit, because the Spirit intercedes for the saints*
> *in accordance with God's will. (Romans 8:26–27)*

Leanne Payne writes of this battle:

> *Those of us who minister to wounded souls realise the*
> *miracle that happens in the life of a sufferer once he or she*
> *gets a true vision of God the Father and the affirming love*
> *of the Father starts streaming towards that person. The*
> *soul of that person will then begin to see and symbolise God*
> *properly; the God of the Scriptures will become his or her*
> *full strength and stronghold.*[10]

She then compares the Christian with the non-Christian approach:

> *We alone have a Saviour of the deep mind and heart, one*
> *who descends into it and becomes its righteousness, its*
> *sanctification, and its holiness.*

The human heart is separated from God, as is the fallen mind. 'The heart is deceitful above all things and beyond cure. Who can understand it? I the Lord search the heart and examine the mind' (Je 17:9–10a).

Leanne Payne continues, regarding the healing of this heart:

> *Jesus first of all comes in and stands in the midst of that*
> *heart. He who is the light of the world illuminates it. He*
> *then speaks the healing word, one which, if received and*
> *acted upon, sets the heart free from all the other dominating*
> *voices: those of the world, the flesh, and the Devil.*

In her prayer ministry she explains what happens:

> *We simply invoke His presence, and then invite Him into*
> *our hearts. He shows us our hearts. In prayer for the healing*
> *of memories, we simply ask our Lord to come to that place*
> *where we were so wounded (or perhaps wounded another).*

> *Forgiving others, and receiving forgiveness, occurs. In*
> *prayer for the healing of the heart from fears, bitterness*
> *etc, we see primal fears as well as the lesser ones dealt with*
> *immediately: those fears that the sufferer often has not been*
> *aware of, never been able to name – they only know that*
> *their lives have been seriously restricted and shaped because*
> *of them – we see imaginations cleansed.*

Counselling tends to be more structured; prayer ministry seeks to allow God to act in ways which may be less structured and less 'predictable'. Leanne Payne writes:

> *The power to heal and to be healed is available because God*
> *Himself is in our midst. His presence and His power are*
> *mysteriously one, and we who live and move and have our*
> *being in God are called to preach, teach and heal in that*
> *spiritual power and authority…we become ministers of God's*
> *healing love and power, therefore, as we learn to invoke the*
> *mighty presence of our Lord, and as we learn to become the*
> *vessels through which he ministers in our midst.*[11]

As the Apostle Paul writes:

> *I pray also that the eyes of your heart may be enlightened*
> *in order that you may know the hope to which he has called*
> *you, the riches of his glorious inheritance in the saints,*
> *and his incomparably great power for us who believe. That*
> *power is like the working of his mighty strength, which*
> *he exerted in Christ when he raised him from the dead….*
> *(Ephesians 1:18–20a)*

Conclusion

This chapter has outlined a range of physical (medical), psychology-cal, sociological and spiritual modes of treatment (see Fig. 5.1).

The suggestions are not exhaustive. What is important to note is that each area of treatment is enhanced by utilisation of the others. This is with the important assumption that such treatment is being carried out by a skilled practitioner.

By becoming more aware of what is available in fields that are normally regarded as outside of their specialisation, practitioners can become more effective. The area of specifically Christian treatments

Fig. 5.1 Influences on the individual[12]

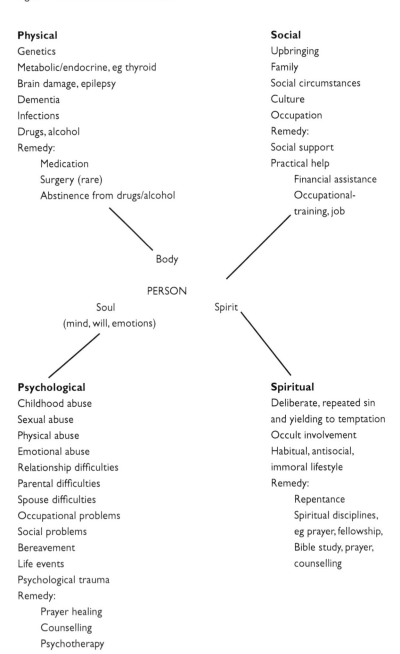

Physical
Genetics
Metabolic/endocrine, eg thyroid
Brain damage, epilepsy
Dementia
Infections
Drugs, alcohol
Remedy:
    Medication
    Surgery (rare)
    Abstinence from drugs/alcohol

Social
Upbringing
Family
Social circumstances
Culture
Occupation
Remedy:
Social support
Practical help
    Financial assistance
    Occupational-
    training, job

Body

PERSON

Soul   Spirit
(mind, will, emotions)

Psychological
Childhood abuse
Sexual abuse
Physical abuse
Emotional abuse
Relationship difficulties
Parental difficulties
Spouse difficulties
Occupational problems
Social problems
Bereavement
Life events
Psychological trauma
Remedy:
    Prayer healing
    Counselling
    Psychotherapy

Spiritual
Deliberate, repeated sin
and yielding to temptation
Occult involvement
Habitual, antisocial,
immoral lifestyle
Remedy:
    Repentance
    Spiritual disciplines,
    eg prayer, fellowship,
    Bible study, prayer,
    counselling

is far from fully understood, and here there is room for increased research and development.

Vignette I

Pamela – Borderline Personality Disorder

> *Pamela is a twenty three year old single woman who feels depressed much of the time. When she was a child her stepfather sexually abused her over a three year period. She has had a number of failed relationships with men. She has difficulties in her regular commitment to her church group and is unable to hold down a job. Sometimes she gets very tense and anxious and the anger she feels leads her to cut her wrists which gives her a feeling of relief from tension.*
>
> *On one occasion she has become very depressed, suicidal and hopeless with profound thoughts of guilt and unworthiness of life and God's love.*

1. Physical factors. There is increasing evidence that there are genetic factors in this condition. However, there is some research that periodic use of medication can be helpful when symptoms or distress are particularly troublesome. For example when she is depressed, antidepressants may be used, and antipsychotics may be used for psychotic episodes and/or severe anxiety.

2. Social factors. The fact that she has been sexually abused may mean that the social context within which she was brought up was deficient. Because of the behaviour exhibited by Pamela, it is likely that she has alienated her friends, family, work colleagues and even church friends to some extent. The emphasis on 'treatment' will be on supporting Pamela to express her distress in more appropriate ways and to provide social structures – friends, groups, activities, occupation – to support her.

3. Psychological factors. This is going to be a key component of treatment because the damage done to Pamela has affected her view of herself. People who have been sexually abused often have a low self esteem as well as strong feelings of anger. An important part of therapy is going to be to teach Pamela to express this anger in an appropriate way, ie not by self harm. This may be in a group where experiences can be shared but will usually involve individual psychotherapy as well. She finds it hard to trust others, especially men. So issues of helping Pamela to trust another person can be explored.

4. Spiritual factors. As well as the psychotherapy she receives it is very likely that Pamela needs counselling with a skilled Christian counsellor and/or prayer ministry. Quite possibly her view of God as Father will have been adversely affected by her experience of abuse. This is likely to require counselling and prayer over a longer time period (eg months) to help Pamela work through some of her emotions currently directed at God. Hopefully she will learn to understand the truths of the gospel and to apply them. In addition, she can slowly begin to adhere to spiritual disciplines such as prayer, Bible reading, fellowship and, where necessary, practise confession and repentance.

For further reading see chapter two.

Vignette 2

Dave – Antisocial Personality Disorder

> *Dave is a twenty five year old man who has joined the church after his release from prison. He had encountered an outreach group from the church and had become a Christian in prison. He had been brought up in a family where both his father and older brothers were involved in theft and burglary.*

> *It is likely that Dave would have been diagnosed with an antisocial personality disorder according to the International Classification of Diseases.[13] If we refer to our model we see that a number of influences may be operating in Dave's life.*

1. Physical factors. There is evidence that antisocial personality disorder is to a small extent inherited (see chapter two).

2. Social factors. These are usually more important than physical factors in Dave's case. The upbringing that he comes from will have influenced his behaviour. There is evidence that modelling plays a major role here. His family will have taught him the behaviour and he will have seen some of the rewards of such. Treatment will need to be focused at changing some of the social factors that influence Dave's life. Now that he has become a Christian the support of his church group will be crucial. He will need help with breaking away from the negative influences. This may well involve practical support with accommodation and occupation and counselling as how to relate to his family and former friends. The way that he thinks about life will need to alter (see Rom 12:1–2).

3. Psychological factors. The principles of operant conditioning apply here in that it is likely that Dave's behaviour will have been rewarded by approbation and monetary reward by his peers and family. Treatment of these factors will often go hand in hand with treatment of the social factors in his life. Psychological treatments have been shown to have some benefits in patients like Dave, especially some group treatments. However, in patients who show a high level of criminality there is a paradoxical worsening of their behaviour after group therapy (see chapter two).

4. Spiritual factors. Again there will be a link with the social factors here. If Dave returns to his previous lifestyle and friends then he will find it hard to resist the temptation to return to his former ways. He will hopefully be finding the help of his church and using his own spiritual disciplines to combat the temptations he will definitely face.

For further reading see chapter two.

Vignette 3

Alan – Bipolar Affective Disorder

> *Alan is a thirty year old writer recently diagnosed with bipolar affective disorder, or manic depression. He has had mood swings most of his adult life and when he was feeling elated in mood he found that he was particularly creative. However, in the last few months he and his wife had been arguing frequently especially after he had confessed to her that he had had sex with a prostitute on one occasion and then he had bought an expensive new car on credit without consulting her. He was also noticing that he could no longer write effectively during his 'highs' and that he was beginning to feel sad and depressed at times.*

1. Physical factors. Alan's mother had bipolar affective disorder. Research shows that there is a tenfold increase in risk for the condition over the normal population, for the children of people with bipolar affective disorder. This risk persists even if the child is adopted away from their biological parent thus demonstrating that the effect is inherited rather than socially acquired. The treatment for the condition is also physical. A very effective medication, lithium, is both a treatment and a prophylaxis (prevention of recurrence) for the condition (as is sodium valproate – see this chapter).

2. Social factors. It is important that Alan and his wife will need support from their friends and family to help them manage Alan's condition.

3. Psychological factors. Because of the strain that Alan's illness and his behaviour have put on the marriage it will be necessary and helpful to have marital therapy. Cognitive behavioural therapy may also be useful for his bipolar affective disorder.

4. Spiritual factors. Alan will need to repent of his unfaithfulness both to God and to his wife. He will need the help of his pastor in this. In the longer term he will need to put into place structures to help prevent him falling into temptation, both financial and sexual. He will practise spiritual disciplines to help in this process.

For further reading of a psychologist's personal struggle with bipolar affective disorder, see Jamison.[14]

Vignette 4

John – Schizophrenia

John is a twenty five year old man whose father has schizophrenia and he developed the illness himself over a year whilst at university. He lives with his parents and is unable to work so stays at home all day. He frequently argues with his mother about the untidy state of his room.

1. Physical factors. Genetic factors have been shown by research to be important in schizophrenia. The child of a schizophrenic parent – even if not brought up with the parent – has a 15 times greater risk of schizophrenia than that for the general population. Physical treatments – antipsychotic medication – have been shown to prevent relapse and to help treat the psychotic symptoms of the illness, such as hallucinations (perceptions without external stimuli, eg voices when no-one is present) and delusions (fixed beliefs unamenable to reason and not in context with the person's culture).

2. Social factors. Research has shown that a lot of close contact with the family, especially if they are critical or over-involved, leads to more likelihood of relapse of the illness. It is important to educate the family not to be overly critical. The number of hours per week of face to face contact may need to be cut down. If these measures are not successful then John could move to a hostel (see Vaughn and Leff [15]). The presence of meaningful occupation is also important. In the developing world the prognosis of schizophrenia is better than in the developed world. It is thought that this may relate to the greater ability of patients in countries such as India, Nigeria and Colombia to find small yet significant employment.

3. Psychological factors. Research has shown that life events do precipitate a relapse in patients with schizophrenia. Supportive psychotherapy can be provided – interpretative psychotherapy is only employed with great care, if at all, because the psychological resources of the person are often fragile due to the illness. The patient is at risk of becoming more paranoid in an intensive psychotherapeutic relationship. Cognitive-behavioural psychotherapy can be very helpful for instance in the treatment of auditory hallucinations (voices) and also to improve the patient's insight into his illness.

4. Spiritual factors. These will mainly be supportive in terms of the fellowship, eg friendships that are unthreatening, calm and practical – helping John not to be isolated but to go to a church/fellowship group that does not impose too many demands on his resources. The spiritual disciplines will be useful although John's concentration will often not be as good as those without his illness, so allowance should be made for this in Bible study, sermons etc. Also, in group Bible studies, the leader and other participants should be aware that John may, at times, be distracted by voices.

Vignette 5

Debbie – Anorexia Nervosa

> *Debbie is a sixteen year old girl from a successful, professional family who believes she is too fat at six stone and 5 ft 6 in. She is more than 15% underweight for her height and her periods have stopped.*

1. Physical factors. The aetiology (causes) of this condition is not known for certain, but it is possible that there is a disturbance of the brain and also genetic factors. It is thought that this is secondary to the weight loss. Patients like Debbie can become depressed and therefore may require antidepressants (see physical treatments above).

2. Social factors. Anorexia nervosa can be construed as an illness of middle class, young women, often in developed countries. There may also be the influence of the fashion industry and certain occupations such as ballet where thinness is valued. Within society, public awareness and re-education can be a treatment in order to convey to the public that the emphasis on thinness can be deleterious to health, as in the case of anorexia nervosa.

3. Psychological factors. These are very important in this case. Many psychological theories have been put forward. One of these theories is that the young woman uses food as a protest – conscious or unconscious – against the perceived demands made on her to achieve success. The cessation of periods has also been seen as a desire on the part of the young woman 'not to grow up into a woman, capable of bearing children'. Family therapy has been shown to be an effective treatment when the patient is under eighteen. After eighteen years individual psychotherapy has been shown to be more effective.

4. Spiritual factors. The general principles of the importance of the spiritual disciplines apply: prayer, Bible study and particularly fellowship with supportive Christians. More intensive prayer counselling may be necessary in some cases.

For further reading see Lovell.[16]

Vignette 6

Louise – Senile Dementia

> *Louise is an eighty year old woman who has been losing her memory for about a year. She fails to recognise certain people and cannot remember where she is at times.*

1. Physical factors. It is known that the cortex of the brain degenerates in those with senile dementia of the Alzheimer type. Recently, anti-dementia medication has been found which alleviates some of the symptoms of the dementia (cholinesterase inhibitors – see physical treatments above). The disease process is not arrested but the symptoms are improved for a period of time.

2. Social factors. It will be important to keep the patient in familiar surroundings and, if it is necessary to provide more intensive care, then an appropriate home should be found. Home help, district nursing and other help can keep the patient at home depending on the level of family and informal carers.

3. Psychological factors. Supportive psychotherapy may be helpful for Louise and possibly for her carers.

4. Spiritual factors. Bible reading, music and worship tapes may be helpful for Louise depending on the degree of the dementia. Demented people may be able to pray relatively coherently even when their conversation does not make rational sense.

Vignette 7

Mary – Agoraphobia

> *Mary is a forty five year old home maker whose children have grown up and left home, and whose husband has a busy manual job. She has developed agoraphobia over the past two years, leading to an inability to leave her house.*

1. Physical factors. These are relatively unimportant, though if Mary develops a depressive illness then antidepressants need to be considered. She may also have put on weight and lost some general fitness so may be feeling tired.

2. Social factors. These are important in the aetiology of the condition. In Mary's case the loss of the mothering role is likely to be influential. This will need to be addressed. She does not have any occupational training so it may be appropriate to aim towards a training of some description.

3. Psychological factors. The mainstay of the treatment will be cognitive behavioural treatment in which exposure therapy will be employed over a period of weeks. Possibly marital therapy may be needed if the strain on the marriage has been considerable.

4. Spiritual factors. The spiritual disciplines will be useful including prayer and Bible study. The location of fellowship meetings will need to be considered, according to her response to treatment.

Readers may find Baker's and Redgrave's books[17] helpful in the management of anxiety disorders.

Vignette 8

Elizabeth – Depression

> Elizabeth is a forty five year old single Christian woman who has had three episodes of depression. She has a good job and no financial worries. Her mother, grandfather and maternal aunt suffered from depression. She lost her mother through suicide when she was six.

1. Physical factors. There are genetic and biochemical factors in the aetiology of depression. Physical treatment will be by means of antidepressant medication. Since Elizabeth has had more than two episodes of depression, lithium or other augmentation (additional) medication will need to be considered depending on the severity of the episodes. Admission to hospital may be necessary if there is a risk of suicide during the episode. If she becomes psychotic, ie loses contact with reality and, for example believes she is responsible for evils in the world, then she will require antipsychotic medication. Occasionally if there is no response to medication, electroconvulsive therapy is used, though this is more common in older patients who cannot tolerate the side-effects of medication.

2. Social factors. Possibly Elizabeth is lonely and there are issues of singleness. These can be addressed by means of emphasising her interests, hobbies and encouraging her to attend clubs and other social activities.

3. Psychological factors. The loss of her mother may require further exploration in a psychotherapeutic setting. Cognitive behavioural therapy is also known to be as effective as medication for mild to moderate depression and is also effective in relapse prevention.

4. Spiritual factors. Again the spiritual disciplines will be helpful, though care will need to be taken not to exacerbate any guilt feelings on Elizabeth's part in the depths of her depression where prayer, fasting and Bible study are concerned. Gentle, understanding and supportive fellowship is crucial. When she is feeling better it may be appropriate to have inner healing to help Elizabeth address the issue of the loss of her mother – depending on how ready she feels for this.

6

Personal responsibility and its relationship to substance misuse

Christopher C H Cook

Addiction is rarely considered as being a form of 'madness', but has often been judged as morally blameworthy, and thus a form of 'badness'. However, a range of physical, psychological and social factors contribute to the aetiology of such disorders, and people are often unaware of the way in which their behaviour is leading them to become addicted.

What is the biblical view of the person who is addicted to alcohol?

What is the relationship between each Christian's struggle with sin and the alcoholic person's struggle with alcohol?

How does an understanding of sin help us understand an individual's struggle with alcohol?

Substance misuse: madness or badness?

Substance misuse is perhaps an unusual area of psychiatry in the context of the theme of this book, in that it deals with a group of people who (by and large) are not 'mad', but who have often been thought of as 'bad'.

Substance abuse does find a place in classifications of mental disorder, such as *DSM-IV*[1] and (under different terminology) *ICD-10*.[2] Furthermore, according to most American psychiatrists, it should be understood not just as a 'disorder', but as a disease. This is also the strongly held perspective of Alcoholics Anonymous (AA) and Narcotics Anonymous (NA). Although the disease concept doesn't actually find an explicit reference in the twelve steps of AA or NA, it is universally accepted in such organisations as being the proper basis for understanding their condition. This dates back to their early understanding of alcoholism as an 'allergy' to alcohol.[3] Although this specific theory is now scientifically discredited, the idea of alcoholism as a metaphorical allergy lingers on, and the disease concept finds new support from theories of genetic predisposition, and altered neurotransmission. However, members of Alcoholics Anonymous do not see themselves as 'mad', except in so far as the language is used in a non-technical sense. For example, the second step of Alcoholics Anonymous states that: 'We came to believe that a Power greater than ourselves could restore us to sanity'.[4]

This might be taken to imply that a drinking alcoholic is 'insane', and many members of AA might say that this is indeed the case. However, if you questioned them carefully concerning this, you would probably find out that they don't mean 'insane' in the sense of 'madness' or psychotic disorder. Nor do they even consider that the alcoholic is suffering from a neurotic disorder or personality disorder as psychiatrists might understand them. Rather, they have a sense of addictive disorders as standing apart in a category of their own. And, of course, addictive disorders are 'treated' within a framework of rational discourse and personal responsibility for recovery, in the various meetings of AA, or the treatment centres of the so-called 'Minnesota Model'.[5]

The prevailing view amongst psychiatrists in the UK is rather different to that of either North American psychiatrists or members of AA, in that they would be less likely to accept the philosophy of AA or the disease concept, and more likely to understand addictive disorders as a form of learned behaviour. However, the end result might not be so different in broad principle, in that the focus of treatment will still be upon counselling, group work and an emphasis upon the need to take personal responsibility for addressing the problem.

In fact, if we take a serious look at the disease concept, despite all its ambiguities and uncertainties, there is a good case to be made for seeing alcoholism, or other forms of addiction, as being 'disease'. However, I do not wish to pursue those arguments here. Whatever conclusion we reach concerning them, and however persuaded the reader might be of their validity, I suspect that we would still agree that this disease (whether or not it is actually a 'disease') does not amount to 'madness'. And the reason for this, I think, is based primarily on a phenomenological assessment.

The phenomenology of alcohol misuse

The so-called *denial* of alcoholism is held with almost delusional intensity, and at times betrays a powerful absence of insight of the alcoholic in respect of their condition. The drinking alcoholic insists that they do not have a problem with their drinking, even when everyone else tells them that they do, and even when all the objective evidence stands against them. Similarly, the so-called *loss of control* (or more properly impairment of control) over drinking behaviour is hardly less striking than the passivity phenomena encountered in some cases of psychosis. Whereas in the latter case the psychotic patient feels compelled to obey delusional outside forces or voices, in the former case, the alcoholic experiences a subjective loss of control over their own drinking behaviour. Even when they have overcome their denial of the problem, and accepted that they should moderate their drinking, they find themselves unable to drink within acceptable limits. It is as though they are somehow compelled to drink more than they should.

We could go on to consider phenomenological parallels between alcoholism and psychosis, on the basis of the phenomena of mood disturbance, paranoia, alcoholic hallucinosis and other psychopathology. However, in practice we strongly resist any classification of alcoholism as psychosis, and I think that this is because we tend to listen more to the stories of those who have recovered than of those who are currently suffering from the condition. Somehow, a transition occurs during the early stages of recovery that brings about a rapid return of insight, which affects the subsequent course of the disorder in a way not seen in the functional psychoses. If alcoholic *denial* begins as a false unshakeable belief, with similar qualities to a delusion, it does at least appear to become shakeable with the course of time. If *loss of control* begins as a failure to control drinking, it still does not prevent lasting abstinence amongst those embarked upon a programme of recovery such as that offered by AA. In the face of this, it is difficult to believe that *denial* was not simply a failure to admit personal responsibility for bad behaviour, and that *loss of control* was not simply failure to resist temptation.

> *For some time, Karen's friends and family had been concerned about her drinking. Her sister had gently told her that she thought she ought to cut down on the amount that she was drinking, and Karen had said that she could cut down if she wanted to, but didn't see the need to, and that she resented the implication that she was 'some kind of wino'. Actually, Karen had several times tried to cut down her consumption of alcohol, but on each occasion had discovered that it soon crept up again. Somehow she always ended up drinking more than she had intended. Her boss at work had told her that she should not drink so much when entertaining clients and Karen had angrily replied that it was his fault for insisting that she take on so many clients, and for putting her under so much stress. In the circumstances he surely couldn't deny her the pleasure of 'one or two' glasses of wine? In any case, she insisted, she drank a lot less than many of her colleagues.*

> *Eventually, however, Karen found that her family didn't visit her anymore and, when a client complained about her behaviour, her boss gave her the sack. A friend who was a member of AA persuaded her to attend one of their meetings and Karen found that she recognised herself in the personal stories that she heard the other members sharing at the meeting. In tears, she finally admitted that she was an alcoholic. Her GP provided a home 'detox', she recognised the need for complete abstinence from alcohol, and she began regular attendance at AA meetings. Looking back on it all some time later she admitted that she had known for a long time that she 'should do something' about her drinking, but hadn't liked to admit that she had a problem. As she worked through the twelve steps of AA she found that she needed to apologise to her sister for her rudeness and ingratitude. She even went back to see her boss to apologise to him, and thanked him for helping her to finally come to terms with what she had been doing to herself and others.*

And now, of course, we are very explicitly using the language of moral accountability. Although AA offers compassion and understanding to its members, seeing them as victims of a disease (albeit victims with a responsibility towards their own 'recovery'), wider society is less generous. Alcoholics are often seen as simply 'bad' rather than 'mad'. This tendency has a very long history in the field of alcoholism (or 'inebriety' as it used to be called) and more recently has been even more popular in discourse about the abuse of illicit substances. However, it has also had its vicissitudes. At different times over the last two hundred years, alcoholics have been considered either as simply 'bad' people, or else as the victims of the 'demon drink', or as victims of an addictive society.[6] But they have never been very popular, and have always attracted stigma and reprobation. If they are not 'mad', it would seem that society has to consider them as being 'bad' – the source of their own troubles, as well as those of many other people, and therefore simply reprehensible. Victims they may or may not be – but sinners they definitely are.

The morality of substance misuse

Substance use is widely accepted as good in many areas of life. The majority of the adult population of the UK drinks alcohol 'in moderation' and derive no harm from it. Although certain drugs are proscribed by law (eg cannabis and cocaine), others are accepted in beverages and foods (ie caffeine and alcohol) or as medication. In theory, controlled drugs are proscribed because they are more harmful. In practice some of the legally available drugs are either the cause of potential harm to virtually all who use them (eg smoking) or else are liable to cause harm in those who are vulnerable or who use them heavily or in the wrong context (eg alcohol). In general, substance use is seen as having become substance 'misuse' when and where it is associated with actual or potential harm. It is this potential for harm, particularly harm to the self and/or other persons, which makes substance misuse a moral matter.

In general, individuals are quite properly considered to be responsible for the decisions that they make concerning substance use. Unless human behaviour is viewed from the perspective of hard determinism, in which case it is entirely due to genes and environment – and 'free will' is an illusion, people can be understood as free to make choices to use or not to use particular substances such as alcohol. On this basis, if they find that their behaviour is actually or potentially harmful to themselves or others, they can be seen as being responsible for changing that behaviour so as not to continue placing themselves or others at risk.

Those who misuse substances, at least from the point at which harm is first evident, are seen as knowingly and deliberately causing harm. Substance misuse is therefore wrong – or to use Christian terminology, it is a sin.

A Christian perspective

Now at this point it is very interesting to step back and view the situation from a specifically Christian perspective. At first, it would seem that the Christian scriptures unambiguously endorse the conclusion that the alcoholic is a 'sinner'. For example, the apostle Paul is especially clear about this in his epistles. Paul specifically lists drunkenness amongst the 'works of the flesh' in his letter to the Galatians: 'sexual immorality, impurity and debauchery; idolatry and witchcraft; hatred, discord, jealousy, fits of rage, selfish ambition, dissensions, factions and envy; drunkenness, orgies and the like' (Gal 5:19–21).

Paul also states quite clearly that drunkards will not inherit the Kingdom of God. In his first letter to the Corinthians, he classes them along with the other wrongdoers who will suffer the same fate: 'Neither the sexually immoral nor idolaters nor adulterers nor male prostitutes nor homosexual offenders nor thieves nor the greedy nor drunkards nor slanderers nor swindlers will inherit the kingdom of God' (1 Cor 6:9–10). On this basis, there would not seem to be much doubt that drunkards are wrongdoers!

It is therefore very easy simply to dismiss drunkenness – and all related drinking problems – as being sin. However, I think that this is where we fall into various traps.

First, this easily leads us into the trap of condemning the alcoholic, along with the sorcerer, the thief and the prostitute, as being evil people who are unlike the rest of us. We conveniently skate over Paul's reference to quarrels, dissensions, factions, anger, envy and greed, ignoring the fact that they are endemic in our churches. We define idolatry in such a way as to be alien to our secular culture, conveniently overlooking our obsession with material goods. We then feel safe within our own sense of self-righteousness, and we can condemn the alcoholics, the homosexuals and the prostitutes as being evil people who, unlike those within the church, are still in need of salvation. Instead of identifying with the alcoholic as someone who experiences, at least in some way or to some degree, the same temptations and struggles as we do, we identify their experience as alien.

Second, we assume that somehow people are personally and solely responsible for their drunkenness. Even if they tell us that they struggle with the desire to continue drinking, we assume that they are not sufficiently motivated to stop, or else that they have not sought or accepted help as they should have done. Worse still, there is even a tendency in some quarters to imagine that if only they became Christians all their problems would be solved. If they are not, then it is because of an underlying spiritual problem – which brings us back to the personal responsibility of the individual concerned. The closest that they might get to being absolved of personal responsibility is the suggestion that is sometimes made within the more extreme charismatic circles that addictions may arise from demonic activity. But the implicit assumption is that we do not have these problems because we have behaved responsibly. Others have these problems because they have chosen wrongly and culpably.

Third, we fail to analyse the nature of the problem. If a drunkard is a sinner, then there is apparently no more to be said about the subject. Having already fallen into the first trap that I have just described, we find no difficulty in analysing other problems – our own problems – in a much more liberal and self-protective manner. For example, dissensions on matters such as the ethics of human sexuality are seen as being due to other people's misuse of scripture, heresy or apostasy, and therefore justify our engagement in the very quarrels, factions, and anger that St Paul condemned. However, when it comes to drunkenness, there is no such analysis – there is no defence for the alcoholic.

The development of drinking problems

In fact, most alcoholics start out on their drinking careers in exactly the same way as do most other members of our society. They are social drinkers who often experienced pressure from others and from society that encouraged their drinking. They never consciously chose to become alcoholics. However, through a series of environmental circumstances, often combined with a genetic predisposition, they found that their drinking became problematic in various ways. It began to affect their health, or their relationships, or their ability to do their job. But they were still encouraged to continue drinking – by their friends and family, by advertisers, and by their own growing experience that alcohol made their worries and problems seem easier to cope with. As their consumption increased, they perhaps became more aware that alcohol was causing their problems rather than relieving them. But – just like you and me in other contexts – they found it difficult to admit to themselves that something they liked was becoming something which was harmful and wrong. By this stage perhaps they did experiment with cutting down, or stopping for a while. But having stopped for a while, it just seemed to prove that they did not have a problem, and so they returned to drinking. Biological symptoms of dependence then began to reinforce their drinking further – and so, eventually, alcohol became the focus and priority of their life.

But of course, this is not what happens to everyone. There is no clear demarcation between those who are alcoholics and those who are not. Some continue in their mildly or occasionally problematic drinking for years, without ever becoming dependent. Others switch in and out of problematic drinking. Some drink modest amounts but experience great harm, and others drink heavily but escape any major problems.

When we begin to look at this complex interplay of different social, psychological and biological factors that contribute to a variety of drinking behaviours, it is less easy to blame the individual and more easy to blame genes or society for the 'sin' of drunkenness. It is also less obvious as to where exactly the personal responsibility of the alcoholic should be located.

- Should the vulnerable individual be held responsible for harmful drinking when most other people drinking in a similar way would experience no harm?
- Should the drinker be held more accountable for the behaviour that led to dependence (even if they did not know that it would have this outcome) or the behaviour that results from dependence (even if the latter has become almost impossible to control)?
- Should occasional or isolated episodes of drunkenness always be seen as wrong, even if they lead to no social, psychological or physical harms, and no other moral culpability, whatsoever?
- Should an individual be held responsible for not recognising more quickly that they needed help?
- Should they only be held responsible at the point where they recognise the need to stop drinking but find it hard to do so?
- Are there circumstances in which behaviour is so strongly constrained by biological, social or psychological pressures, that the individual might not be held morally responsible?

At this point, I would like to emphasise that I am not trying to exonerate the alcoholic of all blame. I believe firmly that we are all responsible for our behaviour (unless perhaps in certain cases of true 'madness' or psychosis) – even if it occurs when we have been drinking. However, I am trying to combat the simplistic view that alcoholics are simply 'bad' people who should have known better, and who are quite unlike the rest of us. I am trying to suggest that their experience is in some ways universal – that it reflects a complex interplay of spiritual, social, psychological and biological factors, and that it represents a struggle of the divided will with competing desires.

The divided will

For example, reading again from St Paul, in chapter seven of his letter to the Romans, we find the following passage:

> ...I am of the flesh, sold into slavery under sin. I do not understand my own actions. For I do not do what I want, but I do the very thing I hate. Now if I do what I do not want, I agree that the law is good. But in fact it is no longer I that do it, but sin that dwells within me. For I know that nothing good dwells within me, that is, in my flesh. I can will what is right, but I cannot do it. For I do not do the good I want, but the evil I do not want is what I do. Now if I do what I do not want, it is no longer I that do it, but sin that dwells within me. So I find it to be a law that when I want to do what is good, evil lies close at hand. For I delight in the law of God in my inmost self, but I see in my members another law at war with the law of my mind, making me captive to the law of sin that dwells in my members. (Romans 7:14–23; NRSV)

How many of us would not identify with Paul's analysis of the struggle that takes place within us in relation to sin? In what way is this different from the experience of the alcoholic who knows that she wants to stop drinking, and yet struggles to do so?

St Augustine also has some interesting contributions to make here. For example, in his *Confessions,* he talks of a divided will in similar terms to St Paul:

> While I was deliberating whether I would serve the Lord my God now, as I had long purposed to do, it was I who

willed and it was also I who was unwilling. In either case,
it was I. I neither willed with my whole will nor was I
wholly unwilling. And so I was at war with myself and
torn apart by myself. And this strife was against my will;
yet it did not show the presence of another mind, but the
punishment of my own. Thus it was no more I who did
it, but the sin that dwelt in me – the punishment of a sin
freely committed by Adam, and I was a son of Adam.[7]

If we substituted the desire of the alcoholic for alcohol in the place of Augustine's resistance to serving God, how alien to the experience of the alcoholic would the resulting text be? Let us read this text again:

While I was deliberating whether I would give up drinking *now, as I had long purposed to do, it was I who*
willed and it was also I who was unwilling. In either case,
it was I. I neither willed with my whole will nor was I
wholly unwilling. And so I was at war with myself and
torn apart by myself. And this strife was against my will;
yet it did not show the presence of another mind, but the
punishment of my own. Thus it was no more I who did
it, but the sin that dwelt in me – the punishment of a sin
freely committed by Adam, and I was a son of Adam.

It was only necessary to change a few words of Augustine's original text (replaced by those not in italics), relating to the object of the struggle, and the passage becomes almost perfectly understandable as a description of the plight of the alcoholic.

Of course, there might be some Christians who would struggle with the Augustinian concept of original sin, which is alluded to in this passage. However, in a recent and important work entitled *Bound to Sin*, Alistair McFadyen takes the concrete examples of the Holocaust and childhood sexual abuse as occurrences that no-one would dispute as being sinful.[8] He shows, I think very convincingly, that the Augustinian concept of original sin actually helps us to understand why apparently innocent people who are victims of such extreme situations are 'bound to sin' and why it is that a concept of personal responsibility alone does not adequately explain their experience. I do not agree with all of his arguments, or all of his conclusions, but I think that we must be challenged by his attempt to show that we have over-emphasised the importance of personal and individual responsibility in our contemporary understanding of sin.

Returning to my main theme here, I would argue that popular Christian attitudes towards alcoholism have tended to see the alcoholic as the personally culpable sinner, whose behaviour and experience is quite different to the rest of us. I would wish to argue, in contrast, that the experience of the alcoholic is a specific example of the universal human experience of sin. We will, I believe, be more able to help the alcoholic if we recognise that in many ways we share his or her struggles – albeit in other areas of life, and albeit perhaps not to the same degree.

Sin, desire and addiction

In fact, I think that the addictions paradigm is a useful model to assist theology in its understanding of sin. It reveals much more clearly than is often apparent that the spiritual issue of sin is inseparable from the psychological and biological experiences of human life, along with their social and physical context. On a daily basis, we all experience a range of different desires, which compete with each other more or less successfully. Some we indulge and others we do not. Some we indulge occasionally and others regularly. Some we become rather attached to – or perhaps addicted to. Amongst those that we indulge are those which carry moral connotations of right or wrong. For each of us, the variety and strength of these desires and attachments is likely to be different.

However, we all face the central challenge that confronted Augustine. Will we desire to serve the Lord our God,* and what priority will we give to this desire? Ultimately, this will be weighed against all the other desires that we face, regardless of what they might specifically be. For Augustine, the central challenge to this desire was his desire for sexual fulfilment. In passing, I have to say that I think that the specific nature of this conflict, and the way in which he eventually confronted it by choosing to become celibate, has had unfortunate consequences for a millennium and a half of Christian theology and its attitudes towards human sexuality. But, more to the point here, there are those who would now argue that sexual behaviour also follows patterns of addiction, abuse and dependence that are not dissimilar to substance abuse and dependence.

---

* I am assuming here a theistic position. Of course, the atheist or agnostic might not agree that this is a universal choice. However, even for the ardent atheist, the experience of perceived choices between moral (and perhaps broadly spiritual) values and those of conflicting subjective desires must still be a commonplace occurrence.

We could think of many other examples of desire and attachment – of materialism, workaholism, gluttony, hedonism and so on. For different individuals in different societies, the specific desires that assume priority will be differently determined by biology, psychology, and the material and social environment with its array of available attractions. For some, alcohol might assume the greatest attraction, and for others it might be sex. For all of us, these desires will compete with each other, and ultimately with that central desire that Augustine identified – the restlessness which will only find its rest in God himself. The specific choices that we will each have to make will be different – but the ultimate choice, at least according to a Christian view – is the same for us all. We either serve the objects of our own desire, or we find freedom in the service of God.

The grace of God and salvation from addiction

If we all face this Augustinian struggle of our will against itself, in the face of competing desires and attachments, we might well ask what the solution is: who will set us free? And if, as I am arguing, the experience of the addict is not far removed from the experience of us all, then this also becomes a question about the treatment of addiction. Or rather – the treatment of addiction, when translated into the terminology of Christian theology, becomes a question of salvation, and not a question about treatment at all. The answer cannot be a matter of personal responsibility alone. It is not simply a question of 'pulling ourselves together' or determining that we will do better, for that is the very solution which I have argued has proved so inadequate to all of us in our various personal experiences.

Both Paul and Augustine recognised that our salvation ultimately depends upon the grace of God. We all ultimately need the grace of God to be freed from our struggles with desire and attachment. I believe that this is true for every one of us – whether we are formally recognised as being 'addicted' or not. But it is certainly no less true of the addict. Therefore, whilst I recognise an important place for psychological, social and physical treatments in the addictions, I would wish to argue that in many cases this alone is not enough. Perhaps this is the reason why, in comparison with other areas of mental heath, so many more treatment programmes in the addictions have recognised the need for a spiritual component of care.

On the other hand, I am not suggesting that spiritual salvation alone is the simple and instant solution to addictive disorders. In fact, I think that it is nonsense to talk about 'spiritual salvation' as though such a thing could occur without attention to the psychological, social or biological aspects of our experience of life as fully human beings. However, I do think that the treatment of addictive disorders presents Christian theology with a challenge. How do we understand the salvation won for us by the incarnate Christ in the context of our contemporary understanding of human kind as spiritual beings engaged in a bio-psycho-social experience of life in this world?

As a Christian, I believe strongly that the answer to this question is inseparable from the person of Christ himself. However, in theological terms, I believe that the answer requires a subjective as well as objective understanding of the atonement. That is, I believe that it has to do with an encounter with Christ in the midst of the suffering of our present subjective experience, and not only with the past objective event of the crucifixion of Jesus of Nazareth.

I would like to close with a quotation from Gerry May, a psychiatrist and spiritual director in the USA, author of *Addiction and Grace*. Having reviewed the psychological, neurological and theological nature of addiction, he cautions us against simple solutions. But he especially encourages us not to neglect the spiritual dimension of addictive disorders:

> *Addiction cannot be defeated by the human will acting on its own, nor by the human will opting out and turning everything over to the divine will. Instead, the power of grace flows most fully when human will chooses to act in harmony with divine will. In practical terms, this means staying in a situation, being willing to confront it as it is, remaining responsible for the choices one makes in response to it, but at the same time turning to God's grace, protection, and guidance as the ground for one's choices and behaviour.*[9]

This, I would like to suggest, is the true place of personal human responsibility in relationship to substance abuse.

7

Demons and evil in a Christian context

Roger C S Moss

Psychiatrists derive their presuppositions from scientific observation and method. What are they to make of demons and evil – phenomena derived from the Bible, but often taken to be metaphysical in nature?

Does their remit reach into this domain?

Is there empirical evidence to draw upon?

How are psychiatrists to address the plight of individuals who are said to be demonised?

What is the biblical view of demons?

What is the definition of oppression and possession?

Are there specific 'points of entry' where demons may enter a person?

What allows demons to stay?

What is the relationship between insanity and demonisation?

Can Christians be demonised?

What can be done if you believe someone is demonised?

What are some of the ethical issues specifically for psychiatrists in the area of demons and evil?

Why do psychiatrists see people who are demonised relatively rarely?

What is the biblical view of demons?

The text

There are over 100 references to demons* and unclean spirits in the Old and New Testaments, but there are grounds for believing that demon possession was more of an issue in the times of Jesus because he chose to confront the powers of darkness as a visible demonstration of his role on earth. There are seven accounts of exorcism given in some detail in the New Testament. Not only did Jesus practice exorcism himself, but he specifically authorised his disciples to do so.[1]

The plot

> *The reason the Son of God appeared was to destroy*
> *the devil's work.*[2]

Jesus dealt with demons without magic or performance. He gave the demons simple commands to get out, or to go. There seems to be a clear basic distinction between those considered to be ill and those who were demonised, though in some cases – but not all – illnesses were regarded as demonically caused.

Evil

It is important from a theological perspective that the enormous impact of evil upon the creation is acknowledged. It is fitting for Christians to be sober and realistic in assessing its reality.[3] But Christian theology also maintains that the saving work of Christ in dying and rising established Christ's enduring power over sin and Satan, and in the long run set in motion their destruction.[4]

Sources

A biblical view of demons should not rely on material derived from subjects of deliverance/exorcism. This has been called 'inside information'.[5] There may be some value from a cultural point of view in tracing the characteristics of what are believed to be demons by

---

*   There is only one usage of the Greek word δαιμων (*daimon*) in the New Testament (Mt 8:31), the commonest terms being δαιμονιον (*daimonion*) and πνευμα (*pneuma*, spirit) qualified by various words meaning unclean. Demons were basically the antithesis of angels, and the term refers to spiritual beings hostile to God and humankind. The New Testament resists the Greek tendency to regard demons as minor deities and dispels fear of the demonic, yet it conveys the sense that demons are sinister as they may attack us both spiritually and physically in the service of Satan.

the subjects or the voices that appear to speak through them. But to assume that this phenomenon has a precise continuity with what prevailed in Jesus' time is not warranted; cultural assumptions have changed. On general biblical principles it should be expected that demons are unreliable and a source of confusion, and therefore hardly to be trusted in what they appear to say about themselves.

Symbol

It is important here to make the basic observation that the word 'demon' is at least a symbol for a way of thinking about evil. It does manage to incorporate the reality of evil, and the way evil seems to affect people, even to dominate their behaviour at times. It catches a sense that evil can seem wilful and cunning, rather like a devious or bad person. But without diminishing the seriousness of evil, we do have to distinguish the way we conceptualise our lifelong vulnerability to evil from the symbols that different cultures use to convey such spiritual truths. When the Bible or Bible believers use such a word, it is arguably more important to uphold the truths it represents than to reify – to confer concrete reality on to – the symbol, which in any case varies from culture to culture and from one age to another. So the biblical view should not simply be rejected as belonging to an outdated worldview. Its symbols actually refer to core truths that many Christians are still content to own as part of their contemporary Christian faith.

Symbols and reality

'But are demons real?' is the question that persists after my carefully chosen phrases in the last paragraph. Of course, a symbol can be an object that has objective reality, but does what it represents have objective reality too? A psychiatrist needs to work out whether someone who claims to believe in demons is holding a false belief (if demons are not 'real'), or whether they hold a belief whose 'reality' is shared with others who appear to be sane individuals. Sims[6] helpfully recommends 1 Corinthians 10:14–22 for a way to distinguish layers of reality. Here Paul has been discussing temptation, and promising that God provides a way out, so long as sensible believers do not court temptation through any form of worship of idols that take the place of God. Eating sacrifices offered to idols amounts to the same thing as breaking bread and drinking the cup at the Lord's Supper – it involves participation that shows unmistakably where our allegiance lies. An idol is nothing, but the demons that represent pagan gods are 'real' alternatives to the worship of God. Clearly, many people worship gods other than the true God, and this belief has its own reality: it is not technically a delusion.

Cross-cultural background – the middle zone

Demons have a reduced or even non-existent place in Western society, but are a part of the normal explanation for many of life's perplexities in traditional societies. In the modernist view of the world, which we are now beginning to leave behind us, dualism resulted in what has been called the secularisation of science and the mystification of religion. To be left with only a materialist view of science and an otherworldly view of religion excludes a middle tier that still has explanatory power in many cultures today. A belief in demons surfaces in many cultures (including that of the New Testament), and is most easily understood as within this middle tier.

The middle zone[7] sits between a zone of high religion, which accounts for cosmic beings (God, gods, angels, demons and spirits) and cosmic forces (kismet, fate, karma, etc); and a zone of natural science, based on sensory observation of this world and universe, and on the interaction of human beings and natural forces. The middle zone of low religion comprises: local gods and goddesses, ancestors and ghosts, demons and evil spirits, and dead saints – if you look at it relationally; and magic and astrology, charms, magical rites, the evil eye, etc – if you look at it impersonally and mechanistically.

The middle zone is above natural explanation, but at the same time it is this-worldly. The middle zone understands and prevents misfortunes, it makes sense of illness and congenital defects, and it copes with failures in business, crops, marriage or interpersonal relationships. So it concentrates on the power issues of life, health, suffering, fortune, safety, success in love, status, prosperity, controlling the weather, healing of disease and death.

In a word, the middle zone is what folk religion deals with. And it is the willingness to enter into this aspect of cultural experience 'interpathically' that is the secret of a therapeutic relationship, as we would say, with those who find the world problematic. And if the Western reader finds the notion of the middle zone difficult because it is outside his or her normal modes of explanation, then the case is being made for a means of entering into the worldview of other cultures, whether these reside in our own country or abroad. To attempt to foist a 'scientific' view on all of those who come to us for help may not only alienate them, but may also demonstrate our unawareness of factors outside of the scientific purview.

Definition of oppression and possession

Affliction with demons is usually represented by those experienced in dealing with them on some scale of severity, ranging from:

1. No involvement. Temptations emerging from our sinful nature.[8]

2. Temptation by Satan.[9] At this level, a person yields to sinful temptations for a sufficient length of time or in sufficient degree to become susceptible to demonic temptation, meaning submission to an alien personality or entity.

3. Pseudo-possession or possession syndrome. The various terms used to describe a person supposedly affected by demons can be divided into: (a) those that are associated with a psychiatric disorder as the main diagnosis; and (b) those where it is not. The first group (a) may be lumped together as 'possession syndrome' or pseudo-possession or false possession, but this distinction tends not to be observed in the literature. The second group (b) comprises 4. and 5. below.

4. Oppression. Also called demonic influence, demonic subjection or demonic obsession: can be defined as a level of demonic influence more intense than temptations that can be resisted, short of full possession, but reaching a degree where normal life becomes hindered by mental ideation, a preoccupation with evil, or a sense of all-pervading guilt or fear.[10,11]

5. Possession. The phenomenon of an alien presence or spirit entering and taking control of an individual.[12,13] In an amplified form, this could read: 'states in which alterations of behaviour and self presentation are interpreted by the subject *and others* who share his or her culture as due to the presence of another entity, or personality, in the subject'.[14] Oesterreich[15] defines possession as a psychiatric syndrome with several striking characteristics, most notably that 'the patient's organism appears to be invaded by a new personality; it is governed by a strange soul'. Briefly then, '*possession* normally means that a person will appear to be no longer in control of his or her own will, whilst *oppression* indicates a degree of self-control'.[16] Possession is much less common, and Kemp and Williams[17] assert that, as defined by Oesterreich, it is rather rarely encountered today by psychiatrists or psychologists although cases are occasionally reported.[18]

Terminology

Those aware of New Testament Greek often prefer the term *'demonised'* to cover all who are not victims of possession syndrome. Dickason[19] defines demonisation as a general term meaning 'demon caused passivity or control due to a demon's residing within a person, which manifests in various physical and mental disorders and in varying degrees'.

Trance and possession

Halperin[20] distinguishes the terms *trance* and possession, which are often implied to be synonymous in nature. He notes that 'trance' denotes a 'psychophysiological transformation probably involving changes in brain–body chemistry and functioning, such as in the increased production of endorphins or electroencephalogram changes registered during altered states of consciousness. Possession, on the other hand, 'involves cultural–religious conceptions defined via shared ritual practices and belief systems'. Trance induction can occur apart from any notions of spirit possession, just as beliefs of possession can take place without an accompanying trance state. But he finally points out that if the distinction between trance and possession is clearly delineated, then using the fused term trance-possession may have its place when the two sets of phenomena coincide.

Another view

Wilson,[21] a medical doctor and a pastoral theologian, speaking as a twentieth-century Western-cultured man, did not regard people as 'possessed'. He personally felt 'under no pressure to believe in "possession" or "evil spirits" because Jesus believed in them'. His belief in the incarnation meant that Jesus lived in a particular time and place. Wilson is clear that 'exorcism exists in a context of belief; it rests upon theological assumptions'. He concludes:

> *…however we may look at it, and in whatever language we wish to talk about it, 'possession' is some kind of bondage which is cramping a person's full sense of human autonomy. He needs to be helped to 'come to himself', to 'find himself', to 'affirm himself', to 'love himself'. Whether this is achieved by some authoritative command, or by patient counselling, my feeling is that recovery takes place only when the particular help is undergirded by a strong group or congregational life which is founded upon life's normality. 'Possession' or 'Identity Confusion' is some*

*piece of life which has evaded synthesis, and obtained
a power of its own to influence and destroy the person.
The person must be helped to assume responsibility for it,
and this he can only do if other people are willing to assume
responsibility for it and to share it: 'A man is a man by
reason of other people'.*

This is reminiscent of conventional definitions of a delusion as a false belief 'outside the group or culture to which the person belongs'.

Prevalence

90% of 488 societies in all parts of the world studied by Bourgignon[22] had recorded one or more institutionalised, culturally patterned forms of altered states of consciousness. In 52% of the total, such experiences were attributed to possession.

Ross and Joshi[23] found that 2% of the general Canadian population reported a possession experience. Pfeifer[24] extrapolates from his own findings that 2.6% of the total population (of Switzerland) might believe in the possible demonic causation of their problem.

Pfeifer[25] examined a large sample of patients in Switzerland describing themselves as religious, with regard to possible causalities of their symptoms. 37.6% of his sample of 343 believed in the possible causation of their psychiatric problems through evil spirits, and 104 of the 129 (30.3% of the total) had been through a ritual prayer of deliverance or exorcism. Prevalence of such practices was significantly related to diagnosis (anxiety disorders and schizophrenia), to lower educational level and rural origin, and to church affiliation (charismatic free churches).

Pfeifer's conclusion is that beliefs in possession or demonic influence are not confined to delusional disorders and should not be pronounced to be mere delusion. Rather they have to be interpreted against the cultural and religious background that is shaping causal models of mental distress in the individual.

Dynamics

The various definitions of demonisation assume an acceptance both of the existence of demons, and of the notion that a person can be invaded, taken over, or controlled by some independent force or personal spirit. Psychiatrists are used to this latter concept as an explanation adopted by psychotic persons to explain their own chaotic thought processes and experiences, but in people who are not psychotic the mechanism is more akin to a defence mechanism. It seems to coincide with a need to evade responsibility, to appear to be the passive victim, which is indeed a common defensive strategy. Pfeifer quotes Csordas[26] who, in a study of Catholic charismatic healing rituals, notes that behaviours which are not acceptable in a religious culture – such as irregular forms of sexuality, or falsehood – are commonly attributed to demons. And as Trethowan[27] comments, following Freud, it would seem that the most common way in which man divorces himself from his own sense of vileness, as may be aroused by his lust, hate, envy and aggression, is by means of the psychological mechanism of projection. Such a mechanism, Trethowan suggests, is strengthened by a fantasy of evil as something personified. 'In this way the tale as told, all too readily becomes: "It was not I, but the devil made me do it".' More recently, double bind, possession and dissociation have been added to the list of mechanisms.[28]

Dissociation
Castillo[29] has made the claim that dissociation theory (when one aspect of mental functioning, eg memory, is split from the others) offers a better tool for research into pathological spirit possession in South Asia than does either Freudian theory, viewing spirit possession as culturally shaped hysteria, or biologically based theory in contemporary psychiatry. This is because searching for biological factors that cause mental illnesses so often ignores and eliminates the social and cultural aspects of experience. Dissociation theory views spirit possession as an altered state of consciousness, and does not presume psychopathology or unconscious processes which may not be culturally appropriate. It incorporates psychosocial processes and aetiologies that encompass psychological trauma and spontaneous trance reactions to extreme stress, such as child abuse. Trance is seen as an attempt to adapt and survive. Castillo's clinical studies appear to show that Multiple Personality Disorder (now called Dissociative Identity Disorder) in North America has a similar aetiology to spirit possession in South Asia.[30]

Are there specific entry points for demonic oppression? (sin, trauma, abuse etc)

A list of possible mechanisms of entry can be attempted, with the following provisos:

1. The devil is viewed as subtle, confusing, lying and deceitful, and is therefore not subject to rules or patterns.
2. We are talking about the entry of *evil* as well as its more personalised or colourful manifestations.
3. The entry of evil is not necessarily a conscious and deliberate choice, much as we might wish to represent it so.* A good deal of emotional hurt is what is done to me rather than what I choose, and the entry also depends on those who have influenced me maliciously.
4. If evil is inflicted through major abuse, it is possible that amnesia or repression may prevent awareness of the original hurt and its specifically evil nature. The existence of false memory syndrome, and the controversy about it, has taught us that external evidence must be sought before legal blame can be pursued; similarly, great care is needed before presumptions of the mode of entry can be reached.

---

* Individuals are often carelessly described as making a wrong choice, when they have been unconscious of the motivation for their behaviour. This may in fact be no more than an assumed *interpretation* by an observer.

Routes of entry

Virkler[31] categorises two main routes for people to become demonically oppressed. They are the first two broad groups below. I have added details from other writers.

1. Personal, continued involvement in sin without repentance, including:
    (a) occult practices;
    (b) invitation to Satan, demons etc to become involved, especially before accepting Christ;
    (c) personal preoccupations with power, position, wealth and fame;
    (d) a desire for some person, thing or power combined with a willingness to pay the price (cf the classical story of Faust).
2. Family involvement in the occult.
3. Sins committed against the individual:
    (a) childhood hurts – eg powerlessness.
    (b) physical, sexual, psychological and religious abuse.
    (c) curses.
    (d) traumas and accidents.
4. Culture dominated by occult or middle zone thinking without strong Judaeo-Christian cultural influence.
5. Mental illness and personality disturbance.

In the experience of Martin Israel,[32] by profession a pathologist and by calling a priest and spiritual director, demonic attacks are most likely to afflict three types of people:

- those who traffic unwisely in psychic matters, notably trying to make contact with the dead;
- those who use psychic means to predict the future or to do anything else for personal gain;
- those who are afflicted with a malicious hatred against another person or group of people – perhaps resulting in cursing.

So personal choice, and a failure to guard one's spiritual and moral life, play a major role. There are also those whose defences are weakened by what others do to them. Some of these abusers and persecutors act with malign and sometimes consciously evil intent. The extent to which these individuals seek to cover their tracks can make healing a formidable task. The younger the victim, the more that reconstructive learning will be needed in addition to whatever spiritual help may be appropriate.

What allows demons to stay?

Kraft[33] lists the following factors:

1. our Western worldview:
   (a) relegating spiritual realities to superstition and make-believe;
   (b) theologies that teach that Christians cannot be demonised;
   (c) too much emphasis on scientific observation;
   (d) materialism and naturalism;
2. ignorance of evil spirits;
3. failure to deal with internal 'garbage', such as sinful preoccupations and practices;
4. inability to find appropriate help in churches;
5. retaining demons because they grant special powers;
6. demons 'take permission' to stay by virtue of unattended emotional garbage, inheritance, vows, curses and dedications; unforgiveness; traumatic events not worked through;
7. demonic strength can be represented on a scale of 0–10, and people seem to have different levels of tolerance.

Case history

Ann first came to see me for counselling at the age of 50. She wanted help in understanding and getting over her recurrent state of depression. This seemed to have become more prominent in her life since she had become a Christian some four years previously.*

She had suffered from depression, including mild manic spells, over the 20 years since her father had died. She had a significant family history of depression. Her mother had died when Ann was only eleven months old, and the woman her father married six months later resented Ann from the outset, and was persistently bitter and cruel to her. Her maternal grandfather played a part in her upbringing,

* Author's personal case, with patient's permission (name changed).

but after his wife died (when Ann was eleven) he sent Ann back to boarding school. Feeling the rejection in this, she lived a very rebellious existence through her adolescent years, resulting in a hippie lifestyle, cannabis consumption, abortions and lots of involvement in the occult. She said that she got into lots of things for the sheer badness of it. She 'stepped over into evil' and had a hard job getting out of it. She didn't care whom she upset. The occult was 'a power thing'. It promised a lot. It was something with which 'to get back at life', and at people who had used her badly. She had no fear of anything, and was ruthless. She was 'a good actress', used to putting on a smile to cover and deny both her inhibitions and her true feelings of anger and rebellion.

Ann became a Christian four years before she came to me, and was clearly developing a vital relationship with God. Her conversion followed ministry from a minister and his wife who had a good deal of experience in the ministry of deliverance and inner healing. They had been called to her house because Ann was experiencing unexplained feelings of coldness and poltergeist* phenomena. It is the single most frequent cause of appeals for help from the Christian Exorcism Study Group. The cause nearly always lies within the group living in the affected house, and exorcism is not indicated except when there is a serious state of possession.[34] *However, she then faced a long struggle discovering the new identity she was pursuing as a Christian. She was receiving a lot of help from various Christian sources, and there were spells when she was entering into a new sense of fulfilment and purpose in her life. But one of the deeper issues that she knew she had to face was the disastrous relationship she had experienced with her step-mother.*

A few months into counselling with me saw her depressive feelings returning, with nightmares, little sleep, despair, disorientation and a conviction that she would commit suicide. This was partly precipitated by the profound sense of rejection that surfaced when she thought about her step-mother, giving her 'overwhelming feelings of depression and evil'.

---

*   A poltergeist is 'a spirit which makes itself known by noises' (*Oxford English Dictionary*).

Treatment with antidepressants was necessary, and it was six months before she was able to talk through her feelings about her step-mother to the point where they receded in their importance and distress for her. Since then there have been major swings of mood, more issues from her present and past situations to talk through, and a good deal of support in learning to come to terms with her depressive tendency. She says that she had to learn to stop running, and to sort herself out. After occult involvement, in her experience, there is 'always an earthly price to pay'. A move of house, and a change of church, has been important, as has regular psychiatric follow-up from her local mental health service. Most significant has been her determination to proceed with her Christian life and service, and she has found a variety of input and support to assist her in this. I saw her for a total of 39 sessions over two years, and the result is someone almost unrecognisable by comparison with who she was.

Commentary

- Her single-minded commitment to God was a key factor in her recovery, and it somehow endured her most depressive moments.
- I needed to handle carefully the boundaries in my relationship with her – making sure to get her permission before discussing issues with others who were helping her, and being watchful of contacts outside my sessions with her.
- Despite the need to exercise care with boundaries, there was undoubted value in my combined roles as psychiatric counsellor, Christian, being involved in the same church, knowing her main supporters and being able to liaise with them occasionally, and being able to inform her GP as needed.
- The length of follow-up illustrates that while deliverance ministry may be relatively brief, re-adjustment may need to take months or years.
- My psychiatric understanding of the depressive tone of her experience was useful, because its significance sometimes escaped her other carers.
- In spite of these positives, it was by no means an easy experience for her or for me, and therefore perhaps it was good that she came my way at a point in my career when I had gained a wide all round experience of the various problems with which she was struggling.

What is the relationship between insanity and demonisation?

Symptoms of demonic attack

I cite below the criteria culled from the literature by Rosik.[35] But it has to be said that in the clinical experience of Whitwell and Barker[36] these 'classical' features were not strongly in evidence, perhaps partly because their sample of people did not come from groups where these features would have been imbibed. The core of the matter is not so much the behavioural features (which are included here), as the specific and consistent antipathy to God, to Christ and to Christians.

1. **Physical changes**
    (a) changed voice, perhaps a voice purporting to be the demon[37]
    (b) epileptiform convulsions
    (c) violent and antisocial behaviour
    (d) anaesthesia to pain
    (e) superhuman strength[38]
    (f) levitation observed
    (g) poltergeist phenomena

2. **Psychological changes**
    (a) appearance of a separate personality
    (b) individuals experience the entity as not part of themselves
    (c) hearing an internal voice without an associated personality
    (d) confusion or clouding of consciousness
    (e) sudden and complete relief after exorcism
    (f) the individual does not benefit from therapy or medication
    (g) addictive patterns of behaviour
    (h) telepathy, clairvoyance and/or paranormal knowledge
    (i) speaks or understands a previously unknown or unlearned language

3. **Spiritual changes**
    (a) revulsion to the name of Jesus, Christian symbols, and/or prayer
    (b) arrogant, devious attitude
    (c) stark change in moral character
    (d) a professing Christian evidences disinterest in the spiritual, or lack of spiritual growth
    (e) reports occult involvement

Comments

1. Rosik[35] concludes that all but the most sensational of the criteria can potentially be interpreted psychologically as involving the activity of dissociated ego states. This is not to imply that they could not also be features of evil spirits. But the criteria do not possess construct validity (ie they do not exclusively belong to this way of viewing the world) and therefore may not serve a reliable discriminative function.

2. Page: 'The difficulties with developing criteria for making an unequivocal diagnosis appear to be insuperable. Virtually all of the phenomena associated with possession are familiar to psychologists and psychiatrists and generally are explained without reference to the demonic.'[39] Psychiatrist John White has written: 'My own conviction is that science is helpless in the face of the diagnostic problem. I can conceive of no demonic state that cannot be "explained" by a non-demonic hypothesis.'[40] And Andrew Sims quoted Bavington: 'While not wishing to deny the possibility of spirit possession, from my experience of many years in Pakistan I can hardly think of a single case of alleged possession which could not, at the same time, and from a psychiatric perspective, be recognised as either epileptic, hysteria, schizophrenia, or, more rarely, some other diagnostic category. Making such a diagnosis does not of course exclude other possible levels of aetiology'.[41]

3. Page writes: 'Probably the most characteristic feature of the state of possession is the presence of a second personality which overpowers the normal personality of the possessed person and is manifestly evil. Often this alien personality expresses itself in a change of voice and refers to the possessed individual in the third person'.[42] But such symptoms are also found in some dissociative states. He concludes: 'Perhaps the solution is so elusive because the problem has been posed incorrectly. It is often taken for granted that possession must be distinguished from mental illness and that it only exists where psychological explanations are lacking'.[43] The result is a 'demon of the gaps'.

Perry[44] has suggested that explaining human behaviour in demonic and psychological terms may not be mutually exclusive alternatives. And if the two sorts of explanation are complementary, psychotherapy may be as appropriate a form of treatment as exorcism.

Pfeifer[45] also emphasises the value of psychotherapists showing an 'empathic attitude with unconditional regard for the religious values' of their patients, so that a shared model of meaning can be found to support coping. The fact that Jesus cast out demons with a word of command does not imply that this is the only legitimate or effective way of dealing with possession. Some non-medical Christian texts assert that 'deliverance' can take place as part of a 'healing' by various possible means, without a deliverance prayer, as such, needing to be conducted.

Differential diagnosis – decision tree

Augsburger[46] offers a decision tree for differential diagnosis of trance behaviour and possession belief. This tool seeks to differentiate possession from psychosis, neurosis and personality disorders. It allows for multiple causation – the possibility that possession phenomena can occur in conjunction with mental illness and personality disorders. It is useful in showing the steps that need to be taken before deciding how a particular problem is to be handled.

The decision tree starts:
- By isolating organic and psychotic features.
- It then focuses on the presence or absence of voluntary control in order to detect false possession and malingering.
- It then establishes whether or not the trance state is associated with a recognisable person, ritual or group induction phenomenon.
- This leads to determining whether the subject is some kind of practitioner of spirit rituals, or the object of charms or curses or induction of trance by procedures recognised by the group in question.
- What remains is to establish whether religious ideation is predominant over psychological and cultural influences, and whether it is clearly organised to negate the core values or religious setting of that person.
- If not, there is a likelihood of histrionic personality disorder, dissociation or autohypnosis.
- But if the person responds to affirmations of the relevant core faith with explicit negatives, perhaps phrased in deliberate blasphemous utterances, then possession by evil spirits can be deduced.

From this point, we can look briefly at the psychiatric syndromes that frequently need to be considered in relation to possession phenomena. We can then look at the steps that can be taken with regard to demonisation and the ways the intercultural (and perhaps pastoral) counsellor* needs to work with those whose starting point differs from his or her own.

Pfeifer[47] reworked his earlier results and reported that he did not find specific culture-bound syndromes, but could diagnose symptoms according to ordinary psychiatric nosology. A high prevalence of demonic attributions (among people presenting to a special clinic who believed in the possible demonic causation of their problems) was made in schizophrenia (56%) but also in affective disorders (29%), anxiety disorders (48%), personality disorders (37%) – frequently histrionic and borderline types – and adjustment disorders (23%). Evenly across all these categories, 80.6% had sought prayer or exorcism rituals for deliverance. Pfeifer concludes that beliefs in possession or demonic influence are not confined to delusional (psychotic) disorders, and cannot necessarily be regarded as mere delusions. Rather they form part of the complex array of causal attributions given to mental illness, and have to be interpreted against the background of cultural, religious and folklore factors.

Whitwell and Barker[48] studied 16 people who had been admitted as inpatients to a psychiatric hospital over the course of five years, and ascribed a state of possession to themselves. The average age of the sample was 26.4 years, and diagnoses given in hospital were five persons with schizophrenia, nine with affective disorders and two with a neurotic state. Psychodynamic factors contributed to the clinical picture in most of these, and typically involved identity conflicts of late adolescence, with struggles to separate from their families of origin. This is a group of patients that can be distinguished from those who have established links with groups who believe in possession and exorcism, and who do not necessarily show any psychological disturbance.

---

*   Intercultural counselling is the context of Augsburger's work; but this term is extended here to include a worker with counselling skills who bridges not only different cultural understandings, but also the fields of religion and scientific psychology.

Dissociative Identity Disorder (DID), dissociation and hysteria

1. Augsburger says that 'possession as the experience of being controlled by alien intrusive powers can be viewed as the tyranny of a part of the emotional self over the whole. In Western thought this is understood as hysteria. In collective cultures it may be experienced as possession.'[49] Pfeifer[50] notes that, in the decade since Augsburger wrote, there has been something of a paradigm shift from hysteria to the concept of dissociation.[51]

2. Bull, Ellason and Ross[52] in a survey of 236 cases of Multiple Personality Disorder (now termed Dissociative Identity Disorder), 28.6% reported an alter personality as a demon.

Obsessive – Compulsive Disorder (OCD)

Lacy and Khatain[53] provide a case report of a patient with OCD who complained among other symptoms that he was doomed and possibly demon-possessed. He was raised as a fundamentalist Christian, and would not accept treatment with clomipramine* until he had read a Christian book explaining OCD, depression and anxiety on the basis of demonic influence. His symptoms responded well for more than six months to the medication.

Psychotic disorders

1. Schizophrenia. Ahmed[54] studied the nature and content of 51 patients with schizophrenia in Karachi. The majority (34) of the group had delusions with religious and/or magic content, and it was concluded that the dominant role in determining the content of delusions was to be found in general cultural beliefs rather than in the immediate social environment of the patient.

2. Chronic psychosis. Goff *et al*[55] found that 25 out of 61 chronically psychotic outpatients in Massachusetts had significantly more self-reported childhood sexual abuse, higher dissociation scores, more cannabis abuse, more experiences of thought control and more voices heard inside their heads (compared with those with no history of delusional possession). Thus in some psychotic patients, possession beliefs may reflect childhood trauma and dissociation.†

---

*   Clomipramine is an antidepressant drug, with established benefit to some people with obsessional symptoms.
†   See also Whitwell and Barker's finding[48] that continuing conflict with the family of origin – and these are frequently families who place a strong emphasis on religion – sometimes presents with possession beliefs.

When dealing with people who hear voices, I have frequently been able to discern the battle between 'good' (ie which can be interpreted as 'on my side', 'good for me') and 'evil' ('against me', 'bad for me') in the content of what is reported. It seems but a small step, with the help of certain cultural suggestions, for a person to deduce or be persuaded that demons are behind the evil voices.

Conclusion: the relationship between demonisation and insanity

The relationship between demonisation and disturbances of mental health seems to be that the former can nearly always be described in terms of the latter. This does not fully account for the response to exorcism when certain conditions are fulfilled. The involvement of altered states of consciousness, trance states and of dissociation are becoming foci of psychological study.

Now that Dissociative Identity Disorder (DID) has been recognised in *DSM-IV*,[56] its common association with many of those more severely affected by possession states is becoming established, and ways of handling such situations are being evolved. It is also becoming clearer that DID is also a state of post-traumatic stress disorder, following childhood and sexual abuse, and it therefore needs to be established what proportion of demonised individuals (whether or not suffering from DID) have experienced significant abuse in childhood.[57] Rosik[58] has even proposed a hypothesis that childhood trauma may lead to developmental arrest that affects spiritual as well as personal integration. Castillo[59] has identified a spectrum of disorders that represent adaptation to the severe trauma of childhood abuse with such a span of overlapping symptoms that they call into serious question conventional methods of classifying and treating this range of disorders.

Can Christians be demonised?

It may be true that all vital Christians are to some degree 'demonised', when *demonisation* is defined inclusively to cover every phenomenon from temptation to possession. But the ordinary remedy may not be exorcism but counselling into the fullness of Christ,* including an understanding of our authority against demonic agents and a stance of resistance against them in contested areas of the personality.

Dickason[60] examines in detail the *biblical evidence* for and against the demonisation of Christians, and in every case finds that

---

* That is, that a mature integration of all that Christ means in our lives completely 'fills' areas of the personality that might otherwise be committed to other 'gods'.

the evidence is not complete or decisive to resolve the question. He looks at the *theological arguments* for and against, and concludes that it cannot be said with reasonable certainty that either is correct. However, he brings clear evidence from *clinical cases and clinical considerations* that Christians do get demonised and, provided that the research and researchers are reliable, this stands. The analogy with such questions as, 'Can Christians have cancer?' is genuine and useful.* But such research does not create biblical doctrine. Most of the arguments against the demonisation of Christians come from those who deny any demonisation, and who have no hands-on experience of counselling or pastoral care of such people.

Kraft, who brings his core discipline of anthropology to the healing ministry, comments: 'The vast majority of the demons we have found in Christians have entered them before they accepted Christ'.[61] He states that all Christians are tempted, and that we all fall prey to temptation from time to time. Many Christians have encountered the demonic prior to their conversion:

1. perhaps as part of their initial searching for God,
2. perhaps through ancestral links,
3. perhaps through their family situation,
4. perhaps through serious sin that is not confessed and dealt with.

Demons are much more likely to be discovered *after* a person has become a Christian.[62]

What can be done if you believe someone is demonised?

General approach
After interviews with pastoral counsellors from every continent, Augsburger[63] suggests the following guidelines for pastoral counsellors dealing with possession and demonisation. The principles apply across the professional cultures of psychology and theology, as well as across social and racial cultures:

---

* Clearly they can – and their faith does not necessarily protect them from cancer, but this is not explicitly covered in scripture.

1. Be aware of the need for **responsible intervention,** which takes evil as well as illness seriously.
2. **Diagnosis.** Take time to make a careful diagnosis, differentiating mental, social and spiritual phenomena.
3. **Language.** Use culturally adaptive, well-attuned language, concepts and explanations in both psychological and theological diagnoses. 'Emic' constructs (ie from within a given culture, rather than from outside it) and contextually congruent theory are necessary. This is especially the case when dealing with middle zone issues.
4. **Theory and theology.** Experiences of possession by alien personalities, the collective influence of group hypnosis, and the power of rituals, spells, incantations and similar customs in tribal life, do not have precise parallels in Western scientific thought. Be willing to fill the conceptual vacuum in understanding the nuances of these effects with a willingness to appreciate unfamiliar ideas, by the means that follow.
5. **Approach.** Try to see a client in his or her context, to understand the personality in its relational network, and to respect the person's theology in its cultural integrity. This entails flexibility in one's own theological framework and a capacity to enter another person's experience 'interpathically' – adopting a form of empathy towards somebody else when there are no cultural assumptions, values and patterns of thinking in common. This is a key application of a theology of presence – openness to the presence of God in all creation, cultures and creatures.
6. **Methods of healing.** Be open to learn from the healing practices of other cultures, respecting what is integrative, connective and reconciling (as opposed to fragmentary, disconnecting and alienating).
7. **The natural world.** Following the example of the Old Testament prophets, demystify the natural forces – wind, storm, fire, pestilence and earthquake – by bringing them under the dominion of the Creator. (If they are not made sacred, these factors are secularised according to natural science.)

Clinical issues

In dealing with those believed to be demonised, include the following:

1. Evaluation including essential aspects of history-taking and examination by a psychiatrist (and if necessary a psychologist) and by an experienced spiritual pastor. I do not find that God necessarily gives supernatural words of knowledge to those who have the training and experience to discover most of what is required by proper history-taking; and even when I have intuitions that I take to be from God, it is by no means always right to declare or use them immediately.
2. Consideration of the part to be played by psychiatric treatment, counselling, spiritual instruction, forms of psychotherapy and/or 'inner healing'.
3. Multi-disciplinary consultation, with particular regard to confidentiality when this extends beyond clinical staff.
4. An agreed 'treatment' plan, discussed with the person concerned and, if appropriate, with their family.
5. Evaluation of the person's likely response to the authoritative word of a spiritual leader that they respect. While this may be clinically regarded with suspicion as 'suggestion', it is actually a feature of both supportive psychotherapy and of cognitive therapy in responsible hands.
6. Discussion of the advisability of the subject's presence or absence at any ritual, including prayer.
7. Prayer may be considered important but has to be used judiciously in clinical settings; it should be done with one's eyes 'open', not only to the patient's response, but to wider aspects of the clinical environment. It is important to ask for permission, and vital that it is not used to confuse the subject's own responsibilities in the situation.

Psychotherapy

A holistic approach to a person with a mental disturbance that includes signs of demonisation may include drug therapy,[64] psychotherapy, exorcism and pastoral counselling, in a collaborative programme that works out the validity of each resource within its own frame of reference.[65] In view of the risks of misdiagnosis and inappropriate deliverance ministries, it is becoming accepted as good practice to set specific help within a counselling or psychotherapeutic framework.

In particular, psychotherapy may help the individual to look at the origins of various influences – social, psychological and spiritual; to think about their meanings for him or her; to consider the possible merits and risks of different approaches; and to be held within a supportive relationship while standing back from the scene of conflict. It is helpful for the therapist to respect the values and beliefs of the patient as outlined above, but close identification with the patient's particular religion is not necessarily an advantage when he or she needs permission to roam outside its accepted boundaries for a while.

Supportive therapy, family therapy,[66] behavioural approaches[67] and hypnotherapy[68] have been described, though it has to be said that these approaches seem to have been evaluated even less than exorcism (see below). Jerome Frank, doyen of students of different cultural approaches to healing, notes: 'The permeability of the boundary between science and religion in contemporary dominant world-views enables some such therapists [he is reviewing a study of Catholic charismatic healers] to be fluent in the terminology of both psychiatric diagnosis and demonology and to be experts in a variety of psychotherapeutic techniques'.[69] In common with much of the current work on psychotherapy outcomes, it seems just as true in this case that the quality of the therapeutic relationship, the characteristics of the therapist, and the willingness to be flexible in finding appropriate ways to respond, are probably more important than the particular techniques chosen.

Deliverance and exorcism

This section is addressed to a psychiatrist, psychologist or counsellor who has no authority in a pastoral role or particular experience of ministering deliverance. Very few situations are so acute that a careful multi-disciplinary assessment is not possible before any action needs to take place, and it is usually wise, and feasible, to do anything necessary in conjunction with one or more Christians who have experience of this kind of ministry. Major exorcisms are rarely needed. The Church of England's insistence that exorcism should be done only with the express permission of a bishop after medical and spiritual assessment and a detailed report, emphasises the need to be very wary of dangers for the subject of the exorcism as well as for those involved in doing it.

Wilson emphasises '...the absolute necessity of seeing the ministry of deliverance as only one facet of the total commitment to see mankind released from the power of evil and free to live as sons and daughters of God'.[70] It can be dangerous to be inactive – a girl advised to approach her minister by a psychiatrist because she was constantly 'haunted' by her mother, was refused by the minister who said he did not believe these things, and she became profoundly depressed and attempted suicide.

The actual ministry of exorcism, as Wilson calls it, though others would call it deliverance, is perhaps best carried out in a church, preferably in the presence of the patient and his or her relatives and friends. It is not to be seen as divorced from the witness and community of the body of Christ. A simple form of words is used, and a communion service follows. Alternatively, Wilson used the same type of prayer in his medical consulting room, with members of his own family as available, and encouraged the patient to follow this up with a communion service at his or her own church. He emphasises that the ministry is inadequate, even dangerous, unless it leads to a growing relationship with Jesus Christ. This is the same kind of approach as commended and set out in detail in Perry's book.

Empirical findings

Bull, Ellason and Ross[71] describe a retrospective investigation of 47 separate incidents of exorcism carried out on fifteen Dissociative Identity Disorder (DID) patients. Exorcism, when done in a non-coercive fashion and balanced with psychotherapy, was experienced as helpful, but in none did it avoid all need for psychotherapy.* The precise form of the exorcisms is not described, and it is not clear whether they were done by therapists or ministers. However, it was established that it was best done in a way compatible with the patient's spiritual beliefs, and performed in the context of the psychotherapy and integrated with it, and preferably done by people understanding the dynamics of DID. Though needing replication of the work with a large unbiased sample, this paper shows eight therapeutic factors that distinguish between positive and negative outcomes. They conclude that on this evidence there may be a place for exorcism in DID. The authors point out that a therapeutically neutral approach avoids the theological question of the actual existence of demons. The therapist works within the structure of beliefs of the patient. The factors involved are probably of general application to those with diagnoses other than DID, namely:

---

*   Compare also Pfeifer's work summarised below.

1. **The patient's permission was sought before exorcism was conducted.** This may seem obvious to professionals, but is sometimes by-passed on the grounds of supposed urgency, or because a person has approached somebody who does exorcisms, or because the person is deemed to be too much under the power of the devil to be able to give consent. These authors are thus saying that none of these excuses are valid.

2. **Non-coercion.** Those who have very strong beliefs in demons sometimes believe that they have to take on a physical struggle with a demonised individual in order to demonstrate the superior power of God and perhaps to protect the person. This may be spectacular, but it has to be asked whether such behaviour really shows faith in God's power, or an underlying fear of the devil.

3. **Active participation of the patient.** When somebody seems unwilling to take responsibility for themselves, the situation is often more complicated than possession by demons alone. There may be a personality disorder, or the passivity associated with psychosis. A person who remains passive may not develop any strength of will to prevent the harm of further influences, be they demonic or inter-personal, and their passivity may need prior attention.

4. **Understanding** of the dynamics of their neurosis by the exorcist.

5. **Implementation** of the exorcism within the context of psychotherapy.

6. **Compatibility** of the procedure with the patient's spiritual beliefs.

7. **Incorporation** of the patient's belief system.

8. **Encouragement** of patient self-independence regarding exorcism.

Pfeifer[72] also found that although many patients experienced religious rituals as positive, outcome in terms of psychiatric symptomatology was not improved. When the outcome was actually negative, increasing the patient's distress through feelings of guilt, fear, isolation and despair, and even producing or exacerbating psychosis, there were some typical features associated with the attempted exorcism: dogmatic and coercive forms of exorcism (similar to highly directive encounter groups), long and emotional sessions, rejecting other models of distress and exclusion of medical treatment.

Rosik[73] makes a strong and commendable case for outcome studies on exorcism. He gives an indication of possible negative effects and abuses that appear to occur with some regularity after exorcism. He comments: 'If even a relatively small portion of these individuals are experiencing negative sequelae, the cost in terms of human suffering and damage to the church's reputation would still appear incalculable'. He lists the following shortcomings of exorcisms that emerged in the course of clinical practice: residual psychological distress sufficient to seek psychotherapy; abusive and coercive practice of exorcism – including an exorcist who appeared to have a severe personality disorder; and more subtle feelings of being emotionally manipulated and misunderstood, fearing that the subject was evil, along with disappointment, hopelessness and being a failure even after procedures that appeared outwardly successful to the deliverance team. In the latter cases, lasting change in internal distress did not result, but the subjects could not communicate this to the exorcist.

Rosik also summarises Bowman[74] and Fraser[75] who found no lasting beneficial effects of exorcism in 22 cases being treated for dissociative disorders. Rosik criticises the quality of this research, which had led the authors to advise therapists not to involve themselves in such procedures.

Page[76] also lists a number of perils attached to the ministry of exorcism. The dangers he lists are:

1. dehumanisation by diminishing the person's sense of responsibility;
2. unwitting encouragement of the disorders being treated by the power of suggestion, and unconsciously encouraging role enactment;
3. addressing surface needs and ignoring or intensifying deeper needs, thus neglecting the injustice and social problems that underlie the possession syndrome;
4. experience rather than Scripture comes to play a dominant role, and loses the restraint characteristic of biblical teaching on possession and exorcism.

This limited review of some important but as yet incomplete research shows that as with most effective treatment procedures, there are serious risks to avoid. However, there are some possible benefits for exorcism when it is conducted with due regard for accurate diagnosis and the likely need for accompanying psychotherapy.

Some ethical dilemmas raised for psychiatrists by demons and evil

1. ***Cultural respect.*** It would now appear to be unethical to respond to apparent demon possession without taking proper account of its cultural setting and of the part to be played by those who are experienced in healing within that culture, as well as those trained in mental health and pastoral care.

2. ***Research.*** See Rosik.[77]

   a) Outcome studies following exorcism can help bridge the gap between practitioners of exorcism and their secular, professional and religious critics. 'The church has been established to be an agent of healing people, not harming them.' Outcome studies are the more necessary with the growth of our understanding of the post-traumatic effects of child abuse, dissociative theory, and the limitations of anecdotal reports and the potential negative sequelae of exorcism.

   b) Identifying which contemporary possession symptom clusters are best treated using psychotherapy, deliverance or some combination of the two.

   c) Using a growing databank of good research for quality control or audit.

3. ***Collecting evidence.*** With regard to Allison's[78] experience, we need to find ways to give account of our therapeutic activities in the field of demon possession and exorcism that are professionally comprehensible. Research is feasible, even with single-case designs, and the concerns of ethical committees are not for nothing. This is a field where the patient's view and needs must be taken into account, and is one where as yet we cannot be said to have been particularly successful. For example, if it became apparent that evidence-based practice indicated that people in trance states need to be treated by means of altered states of consciousness, hypnosis or the like, how would we proceed with regard to our own attitudes to such methods?

4. ***Interpathic* process***, ie listening to people's own
   social/folk/popular/cultural way of understanding
   themselves without creating barriers by medicalisation
   of terms. What are we doing, ethically, when we contradict
   the assumptions and beliefs of a cultural grouping other than
   our own, whether we do it deliberately or unintentionally?

5. ***Relationships*** with clergy, counsellors, church leaders
   and Christians in caring professions need to be cultivated
   carefully to break down barriers of suspicion. The onus is
   on our own profession (whatever that is) to make efforts
   to understand interpathically. There are of course ethical
   issues to be addressed when doctors work with non-medical
   people in non-professional settings. We need to find ways
   to be available for multi-disciplinary consultation, and to
   familiarise non-professionals with the benefits of an agreed
   treatment plan.

6. ***Between two worlds*** – learning to hold the tension between
   a medical/psychiatric viewpoint and religious/cultural
   viewpoints. It is essential to consider the ethical implications
   of trying to wear two or more hats, eg operating as a
   psychiatrist, and some kind of minister of Christian healing,
   at the same time. Most would advise against it. Even when
   a psychiatrist is accepted in his or her medical role as well
   as being recognised by a given community as a 'minister',
   it is the clarity of these distinct roles to the distressed and
   perhaps disturbed subject of deliverance that deserves most
   consideration. It is usually better for the roles to be played
   out by separate persons, and if both can be present with the
   authority to exercise their roles as necessary, then both the
   spiritual and emotional interests of the subject are likely to
   be safeguarded.

7. ***Bracketing***. Learning to bracket (that is, to suspend acting
   upon) our own personal values while remaining aware of
   them is an ethical necessity. There are times when a greater
   good is at stake than to observe the letter of practices
   we normally adopt.[79] We have to learn to deal with the

---

*   Interpathy is defined as: 'an intentional cognitive envisioning and affective
experiencing of another's thoughts and feelings, even though the thoughts arise
from another process of knowing, the values grow from another frame of moral
reasoning, and the feelings spring from another basis of assumptions. In interpathic
caring, the process of "feeling with" and "thinking with" another requires that one
enter the other's world of assumptions, beliefs, and values and temporarily take
them as one's own.' (see ref. 1, p. 29).

accusations of short-sighted Christians that we may be compromising our faith.

8. **Costs**. May there be an ethical dilemma when exorcism is recognised to be the start of a longer process involving continued care and appropriate psychotherapy, and the costs of the latter seem prohibitive? This especially applies in the case of people with problems of Dissociative Identity Disorder or Borderline Personality Disorder. Taking a responsible position in this sort of ministry means wrestling with such issues before embarking on procedures that might well raise complications at one level or another.

Why do psychiatrists see demonised people relatively rarely?

1. People who believe they are demonised usually tend to look for help from someone who shares their belief about demons. Initially that tends to be within the culture that taught them this belief. They only look outside the group if it fails them, if they are marginal to it, or if their behaviour becomes too extreme for the group to cope with it.[80, 81] The power of suggestion within the subculture, and the altered states of consciousness in which the suggestions are made, are relatively strong, and this serves to bind the person within the group.

2. Demonised persons may be aware that they have become too involved with or too influenced by something evil, so they turn for help to religious and spiritual sources. A pattern likely in the UK at present is that those who present to psychiatric services do not in fact have a trusted basic group, or are endeavouring to make a break with it or with their family.[82]

3. Cultural groups who explain evil by reference to the demonic tend, with some justification, to distrust scientific and psychiatric ways of dealing with behaviour that has moral connotations. They may have established efficient ways of dealing with the manifestations of demonisation, so that others do not have to become involved. Consciously or not, they tend to reject people with manifest psychiatric disturbance at an early stage.[83]

4. It is likely to be the psychological and psychiatric aspects of demonisation that mainly interest a psychiatrist, and patients may not divulge their belief in demons until they feel they are being approached with appropriate understanding. Pfeifer remarks that 'there is a natural reluctance in patients *and* doctors to discuss deep religious convictions'.[84] This particularly affects 'views on causality that could be rejected by the psychiatrist as superstitious'. This judgment about who patients can and cannot share this information with is retained until the effects of the possession state are fairly extreme and disruptive.

Conclusion

In the modern era, demons have habitually been associated with outmoded patterns of thought in Western culture – a prescientific notion now succeeded by more rigorous diagnosis and ontologies. But in many parts of the world the idea persists, not least in parts of our own Western Christian culture. It is proposed in this paper that the popularity of demons as a feature of Christian thought and practice has been retained because:

1. It is a way of referring to the cosmic battle between good and evil that is sometimes fought out on the battlefield of the individual soul.
2. Delivering people from demons seems to follow Jesus' example and commands.
3. It is an appealing aspect of the healing ministry for those who believe God's power needs to be demonstrated to an unbelieving world.

Responding to the phenomenon of demonisation is not as simple as dismissing it in favour of modern psychological concepts. Increasingly we are called to help those in other cultures, either in their own or in our own settings. Moreover, those who practise deliverance in contemporary Christian groups often appear to have an effective ministry at one level, but may not be aware of how to proceed in more complex situations, and need to be able to trust and communicate with Christians who are trained as psychiatrists and psychologists, and equipped to play a part in a multi-dimensional understanding of unusual phenomena. Some clear principles and guidelines for such situations have been offered, and it is suggested that a comprehensive approach to pastoral counselling across cultures provides an appropriate model for interdisciplinary consultation and interpreting the growing literature on demon and spirit possession. It would now appear to be unethical to respond to apparent demon possession without taking proper account of its cultural and religious setting and of the part to be played by those who are experienced in spiritual and social healing within that culture, as well as those trained in mental health and pastoral care.

8

Conclusion to the 'mad' or 'bad' debate

Elizabeth A Guinness

The aim of this book has been to explore the interface between mental illness and religious belief, specifically antisocial behaviour, and the interaction of the psychological and spiritual dimensions not just of sick people but of the human personality.

What is the nature and impact of evil?

What is the ethic of inner intention?

How should sin be understood in psychological terms?

What is the extent of personal responsibility?

What is the impact of spiritual maturity on and the place of forgiveness in healing?

What is the relationship between social morality and mental health?

Separating bad from mad: beliefs about illness

In many parts of the world in more traditional cultures there is a harmonious, often therapeutic relationship between mental illness and religious belief, but in Western civilisation a dichotomy has arisen. What we believe about the causes of illness inevitably influences treatment and also our attitude to the mentally ill. The change from supernatural concepts to biomedical ones has resulted in polarisation. Indeed in the past, fear of mental illness led to mistreatment and cruelty. As chapter one points out, separation of 'mad' and 'bad' was a vital step in allowing humane and effective treatment. However, while immense benefits have resulted from scientific medicine in general, the purely secular approach has left a vacuum – hence the increasing recourse by the public to alternative medicine, or worse, the occult.

The polarisation has produced two extremes. On the one hand, most mental health professionals would not think of bringing spiritual issues into their clinical practice. To some extent this is correct. The patient has come for medical expertise not religious advice. Furthermore there must be a mutual understanding that matters of faith are relevant to the consultation. This might arise naturally if a spiritual history were taken. However, there is scant knowledge on how to use a spiritual healing component even if it was the treatment of choice. The Christian pastoral counselling movement is seeking to rediscover the ancient skills of healing the troubled soul (chapter five). But there is little communication with orthodox psychiatry. At the other extreme is the not infrequent view of Christian people that mental illness results somehow from failure, sin or even demonic influence. This can make it very difficult for Christians to receive psychiatric help. Yet the brain is a physical organ and like any other organ in the body it can go wrong.

The human personality comprises body, mind and spirit. The scientific method was admirably suited to researching bodily disease; psychological disorders required greater refinement, but the spiritual dimension has been little understood. How do we define the spiritual part of human beings? Could it be that which aspires to a Greater Being beyond the self, to which we feel somehow accountable, which we cannot deceive but which satisfies the yearning for meaning in life? Christ taught that the human spirit must be awakened, kindled, born anew by the Holy Spirit of God.

Several writers in this book point out how this separation of mind and spirit is detrimental and how addressing the spiritual side of men and women can help heal. For instance the addict (chapter six) needs the help of a Higher Power to defeat substance abuse (the dictum of Alcoholics Anonymous). Severe dangerous personality disorder (chapter three) is regarded as incurable by the psychiatric establishment. Could a spiritual approach reach the devious embattled soul? The emotionally wounded can respond to 'inner healing' through forgiveness (chapter five). The 'demonised' who have courted the power of evil are trapped by it (chapter seven). They need spiritual release as well as treatment.

Mad and bad:
is personality disorder irredeemable?

Personality disorder is the crux of the mad/bad debate. This is the distortion of character formation due to the interaction of genetic vulnerability and an adverse childhood rearing environment. Such people cannot relate to others appropriately, and cannot manage their lives satisfactorily. They suffer themselves and cause others to suffer. There are many types of personality disorder and varying degrees of disturbance. The extreme forms are the dangerous senseless killers. Are these unfortunate people ill or fundamentally flawed human beings? Whatever it is that makes them so difficult to treat gives us a model for understanding the human expression of evil. Let us consider two types, Antisocial Personality Disorder (ASPD) and Borderline Personality Disorder (BPD). Both types have been damaged in childhood by the folly or abuse of others. If ASPD can be said to have identified with the 'evil aggressor' then BPD is the tragic victim of evil.

All too often BPD is the late result of Significant Harm to personality development from neglect, abuse or trauma in childhood (outlined in chapter two). Such people have shattered personalities. Their inner psychic world is fragmented – they have huge unmet emotional needs yet cannot achieve intimacy nor modulate emotion. They frequently harm themselves yet often dissociate (switch off from reality) because of intolerable inner pain. Chapter seven describes how such people are very vulnerable to involvement in evil because they have so few defences of personality.

ASPD on the other hand presents a different aspect of evil. Their impulsive, reckless disregard of others, their need for instant gratification of desires, their lack of remorse or guilt, all show an inability to take responsibility for inappropriate actions. Chapter two illustrates by means of graphs the genetic predisposition that interacts with harsh and inconsistent family life to produce vulnerability to ASPD. Such people score low on three polygenic (due to many genes) dimensions of mental function. These are concentration and impulse control (producing Attention Deficit Hyperactivity Disorder), empathy (producing social communication weakness on the autistic spectrum) and cerebral underarousal. The poor impulse control means that stopping to think so as to learn from past errors is impaired; so also is postponing gratification. The poor empathy hinders the ability to sense social disapproval or victim distress and therefore adjust behaviour. Underarousal of the brain leads to an intense need to seek excitement. Children with these innate characteristics are seen from time to time in child guidance clinics. However, whether they will develop ASPD depends on many factors, such as the quality of parenting, schooling or neighbourhood. This is the crucial period for prevention. Treatment is possible in childhood.

Chapter three tackles the vexed question of treatability in severe adult personality disorder. Whether they are 'mad' or 'bad' has practical implications. Are they the responsibility of the Health services or the Prisons? Of all male prisoners sentenced by the courts 64% have ASPD. In the special prisons, which hold the dangerous psychopaths, the majority (80–90%) has damaged personalities. In the women's prisons this is borderline personality disorder – the tragic victims of evil. Chapter three is packed with information regarding causation, diagnosis, assessment of dangerousness, management and containment of personality disorder. Medico-legal structures for safeguarding the public are outlined, ie compulsory treatment and preventive detention. A comprehensive research review of possible treatment approaches is given.

Must bad win? Exploring a Christian approach

We can and must have a psychological understanding of people with ASPD. However, unless we take the view of hard determinism (ie it is all due to genes and environment and there is no free will) we must presuppose some capacity to choose right from wrong. What would be Christ's attitude to these troubled and troublesome people? Assuredly he would not regard them as irredeemable. However if there is to be a specifically Christian approach it is essential to harness the full array of psychiatric expertise. Too many mistakes have been made in the past by well meaning religious people. For instance the Millbank penitentiary was a flagship Victorian prison built by enlightened reformers to replace the 'hell-hole' prisons of the nineteenth century. Acting on inadequate knowledge and false supposition they thought that solitary confinement would enable the prisoners to reflect on their wrongdoing and repent. It was a disastrous failure.

Chapter three tentatively explores two Christian approaches. A Christian psychiatrist, Bob Johnson working in Parkhurst prison, which holds the most dangerous men with ASPD, emphasised the application of spiritual values – truth, trust and consent. He found that every one of the 60 murderers and six serial killers had a 'grievous wound from long ago', for which they had never been able to receive support. By getting in touch with this Johnson was able to reduce the violence in the prison. A Christ-like approach invoking the compassion of the Servant King and the power of the Holy Spirit may help to engage the damaged person who is barricaded behind his mental defences. Motivation is crucial if they are to embark upon the long arduous journey of change. The key factors identified by the National Institute for Mental Health in England (NIMHE) for management of personality disorder resemble a Christ-like approach. This does not remove the need for a setting of appropriate controls. In addition therapists and carers will need stamina and resolution. Caring for such severely damaged people is very demanding.

The second example was Jackie Pullinger's remarkable work in Hong Kong with the Triad gangs.[1] She set up a combination of spiritual healing and standard rehabilitation. A powerful charismatic experience of the Holy Spirit initiated detoxification and was followed by removal from the drug scene to a therapeutic community setting with job training. Chapter seven quotes a fascinating case history illustrating demon possession in a woman who had had an abused childhood and a chaotic adult life. It demonstrates how spiritual healing needs to be part of a comprehensive treatment plan. This may involve psychiatric medication or psychological therapies but must also include belonging to a strong normal social group, such as a church fellowship. The systemic pressures to conform will both empower and constrain the damaged person. Moreover the burden of care needs to be shared.

Evil, sin or just bad behaviour: sin in theological and psychological terms

Several chapters tackle evil both on the individual and the national level. Is evil a spiritual force or simply the extremes of wickedness, the human propensity for unbridled passions, the 'id' left unchecked? Freud divided the mind into three parts, the ego which deals with conscious reality, the superego which is the conscience and the 'id' which is the instinctive biological drives. The conscience develops in childhood as the child gradually achieves control by conforming with the social norms, the 'rules of the family system'. Right and wrong is learnt as much from example and from nonverbal shame or approval as from verbal instruction. Precisely what is regarded as right or wrong varies according to culture but is strongly influenced by the religion of that culture.

Two of the three major monotheistic religions, Judaism and Christianity, regard the Pentateuch, the five books of Moses in the Old Testament, as the source of moral authority ordained by God. Sin is a theological concept defined as the infringement of God's Law. In spiritual terms sin is what separates us from God. In psychological terms it is the failure of the conscience to control desires and weaknesses. Repeated indulgence in wrong doing sears the conscience and creates a bondage to evil. The more you give in to a bad habit the more it enslaves you. Perhaps the difference between sin and evil is one of attitude. Sin implies an awareness of God and what he requires. The sinner struggles and fails repeatedly because of his human condition. Whereas the central defect of evil in spiritual terms is the repeated and deliberate flouting of God's Law. In psychological terms it is the abandonment of conscience. Chapter seven describes the effect on mental health of courting evil, seeking its power to control and manipulate others. Those who indulge in the occult are particularly vulnerable. At the extreme evil can seem like a supernatural force opposed to God and to all things good. Indeed this is how the Bible depicts evil, personified as Satan.

Bad lurks deep: the ethic of inner intention

Christ defined sin more closely when he taught the ethic of inner intention. 'You have heard that it was said, "Do not commit adultery." But I tell you that anyone who looks at a woman lustfully has already committed adultery with her in his heart.' (Mt 5:27,28) It is the inner intention that motivates the deed. Philip Yancey in his book *The Jesus I never knew*[2] discusses the impossible ideal presented in the Sermon on the Mount where anger is equated with murder, lust with adultery and coveting with theft. Christ did not teach this to produce despair but to show that God looks not just on the outward appearances but on what is inside, in one's heart, one's inner intentions. Christ was also defining sin in psychological as well as behavioural terms. Sin is not only breaking the Mosaic law, but also involves the attitude of the heart. It is interesting to note here that Christ blends the psychological and spiritual dimensions seamlessly together. Anger, lust and greed would in modern thought be regarded as morally neutral psychological responses, the biological drives for survival. Indeed each has its place in the right context. Yet wrongfully applied they become sin, spiritual barriers in approaching God. 'Blessed are the pure in heart, for they will see God.' (Mt 5:8).

What relevance does the ethic of inner intention have for the mental health of society? Modern post-Christian society rejects Christ's impossible ethical standard. Yet most cultures have social conventions for controlling human passions. For instance, in former more intact Christian societies there were strong social sanctions and customs for containing lust. These included the supervision and protection of young women by chaperonage, expectations of honourable behaviour in men, the sanctity of marriage; even the stigma of illegitimacy had a preventative function like pain protecting the body. What is the effect of losing these social safeguards? Nowadays, far from human passions being contained, they are actually exploited by the media, in TV sex and violence, and in the materialism presented by advertisements. Chapter two discusses the impact of this in changing the ground rules of society (shaping the values of the suprasystem) and thus contributing to the breakdown of family life and ultimately impairing the mental health of the next generation.

Another aspect of the 'mad/bad' interface is the distortion of inner intentions during mental illness. The gloomy thinking of people with depression, the morbid jealousy of those with alcohol problems, the misdirected paranoid fears of the psychotic patient can all result in abnormal even dangerous behaviour. The morbid preoccupation with lust in the man with a sexual deviance, fuelled these days by internet pornography, can result in horrific child abuse. Exploring the inner intentions, thought patterns and preoccupations of the patient is an important part of the mental state examination in assessing risk and in judging criminal behaviour.

The criminal justice system regards the ethic of inner intention as crucial for understanding the crime and the appropriateness of punishment. Intent is central to legal responsibility. Chapter four describes how the biblical moral code has informed the British justice system. An example is the command in Deuteronomy for safe haven cities to be set up as refuges for those who had killed by accident without 'malice aforethought' (Dt 4:41–42). This was an example of the mercy of God tempering the savagery of blood feuds in ancient society. 'Malice aforethought' is now a legal principle in the distinction between murder and manslaughter. It is the internal attitude, not only the deed, which counts. This is the *mens rea*, or the guilty mind, the intention. However the Law recognises degrees of responsibility. Intent is assumed unless proved otherwise, eg mistake, provocation, duress, insanity or self defence. Diminished responsibility for homicide in law due to 'unsound mind' is considered after the court has found guilt. It mitigates the sentencing but does not excuse the crime. This is an important principle, which helps us understand God's judgment. So often nowadays people think, 'Why cannot God just forgive the sinner; he can't really help it…Why was the Cross necessary?' Justice in society must be upheld or it becomes meaningless.

Yet God also recognises degrees of responsibility. Judgment will be stricter for those with greater gifts and influence. 'From everyone who has been given much, much will be demanded' (Lk 12:48). God in his mercy judges according to ability and opportunity, ie according to nature and nurture. Mental health professionals are taught to be non-judgmental towards patients. Indeed moral judgments about sin may seem meaningless for those with 'rotten genes and a rotten childhood'. Yet to deny someone personal responsibility for their actions is to make them less than human. It is sin, flouting God's law, which prevents us 'tuning in to God'. Even the simple minded have a spiritual capacity. Christ said, 'Let the little children come to me…' (Mt 19:14).

Dogged by bad: the inevitability of sin

The ethic of inner intention poses a real dilemma. Whereas the law is needed to inform the conscience of the individual and the moral structure of society, the 'flesh' (or the 'id') is helpless to obey. Inner desires require something more radical – strength from beyond the self. For everyone this is supplied to a variable extent by pressure to conform to the social group, family or wider society.

To understand sin in psychological terms it is useful to consider the strands of personality that help or hinder. Some people find it a great deal easier to succeed in life, be good citizens, to relate harmoniously etc. Chapter two describes the complex interweaving of three factors in the developing personality. First are the polygenic dimensions of mental function (intelligence, empathy, impulse control, mood etc). Second is the imprinting upon the brain in early childhood of primary attachments and habits. Third is the impact of the social system (family or cultural group) in terms of beliefs, constraints and expectations. It is these factors that drive the inner intention. When the development of personality goes wrong because of deficits and adversities in these factors, a greater or lesser degree of personality disturbance results. This may be full-blown disorder as was described for ASPD and BPD, or it may be quite minor. None of us is perfect. We all have some quirks of personality. We all need the constraints of the social group.

The spiritual battle is fought on somewhat different grounds. This is illustrated by St Paul's anguished struggles to keep the spirit of the law, not only the letter. 'I do not understand what I do. For what I want to do I do not do, but what I hate I do' (Rom 7:7–25). St Paul was blameless under the law but he struggled with the ethic of inner intention. His realisation of the full meaning of 'justification by faith' was a shout of triumph! Centuries later it became the great theme of the Reformation when it was rediscovered by Luther. Yancey reframes it thus: faced with the impossible standards of the Sermon on the Mount we have nowhere to land but in the safety net of absolute grace. Moreover Christ promised other resources. The Counsellor, his own Holy Spirit, would live within us: 'I will not leave you as orphans; I will come to you' (Jn 14:18). Also 'I am the true vine…No branch can bear fruit by itself…Neither can you bear fruit unless you remain in me' (Jn 15:1–4).

It is perhaps relevant to the 'Mad or Bad' debate that St Paul's struggle is quoted in several chapters of this book. Chapter six develops the theme in the light of personal responsibility.

Hoodwinked by mad: barriers to spiritual maturity

To progress in spiritual maturity we must understand our own psychological makeup. As the ancient Greeks used to say, '*gnowthe se auton*' – 'know thyself'. It is possible to have a 'neurotic relationship with God', to see him as we want to see him, 'in our own image' as it were. 'Neurotic' in this context means that we perceive people not as they really are but in the light of an earlier dominating relationship (the imprinted image). For instance, if one's father had been violent one might see all men as potentially violent regardless of the evidence. Previous experiences, unmet needs and yearnings will colour our relationship with God. We might invest in our faith in God what we need psychologically. Indeed religious faith can become inextricably bound up with the mental defence mechanisms of the mind. The more primitive of these defences, such as denial, magical thinking and regression, lead to our 'kidding' ourselves. We avoid facing painful or arduous issues. At best faith becomes an anxiety management strategy. At worst we project our problems onto others; impute to others our angry negative feelings (projective defence). This makes it much more difficult to forgive others. How much is it possible to change this, to take personal responsibility for ourselves?

Bad versus mad: personal responsibility

Professor Cook is both an ordained minister and a university professor in the psychiatry of alcohol abuse. He brings these dual insights to a fascinating essay (chapter six) on the parallels between fighting addiction and overcoming 'original sin'. The predicament of the addict is comparable to anyone finding himself compulsively drawn to behaviour that is morally wrong. Denial, much prevarication, loss of control, finally leads to a situation whence they cannot extricate themselves unaided. Society regards them as bad and expects them to take responsibility for themselves. Yet, they are enslaved by a chemical in their brain. Alcoholics Anonymous recognises the need for a spiritual component, a Higher Power beyond the self that empowers the addict one day at a time to defeat their craving. From an atheistic position this may be regarded simply as an externalisation strategy, which in neurological terms makes good sense. However, let us think beyond this.

The addictions paradigm provides a model for understanding the spiritual issue of sin in humans as tripartite beings, comprising body, mind and spirit. Humans are physical organisms and as such are driven by the instinctive urges for survival, hunger, sex etc. We are also intelligent beings with a complex psychological apparatus. Third we have the capacity, if we choose, to be in tune with our Creator. We are 'made in the image of God'. Sin, ie flouting God's Law, prevents us 'tuning in'.

'Original sin' is an ancient term used by St Augustine to describe the struggle of the divided will with competing desires, 'the flesh'. Do we serve the objects of our desire or do we find freedom in the service of God? Is this any more possible than the alcoholic exerting willpower? Personal responsibility has its limits. Rational discourse, good intentions and will power are not enough. The solution of pulling ourselves together does not work. We all need the grace of God to be freed from our struggle with desires and attachments. '...for all have sinned and fall short of the glory of God, and are justified freely by his grace through the redemption that came by Christ Jesus' (Rom 3:23–24). Yet this is not simply instant salvation related to an historical event when Christ was executed by the Romans. It requires a daily grasping of what Christ did on the Cross.

The power of grace flows most fully when the human will chooses to act in harmony with the Divine Will. This is where personal responsibility lies, in this choice. Several chapters develop this theme. Chapter three points out that personal responsibility is a moral issue rather than scientific. Taking responsibility for sin is a crucial aspect of spiritual maturity. In resisting evil, each decision for right strengthens the next (and vice versa) until it is easier to choose the right rather than the wrong. This is comparable to the one-day-at-a-time battle for the alcoholic. The sinner must engage in step by step conscious resistance to evil through daily encounter with the grace of God. This actually makes good sense in neurological terms because constant repetition will realign brain pathways. In theological terms it is what St Paul calls '[working] out your salvation with fear and trembling' (Phil 2:12–13) or running the straight [narrow] race (1 Cor 9:24–27). Although justification by faith is instant at conversion the practical outworking is a steady grind that leads to spiritual growth.

Condemned to be bad by mad: the terrible dilemma of the paedophile

Beer in chapter three discusses the plight of the paedophilic offender who has found faith in God and wants to join a church congregation. His faith will not immediately change the forces which drove him into paedophilia. He will have to face the daily battle with the inner intention or craving just like the alcoholic patient. What made him addicted to paedophilia will include wrong done to him by others (see chapter two). Very likely he has a 'grievous wound from long ago' such as sexual abuse as a child so that his sexual development was distorted. He would have learned never to trust other people and would find it difficult to form rewarding attachments. Alternatively he may lack empathy in an autistic way and be unable to form intimate friendships, which are the healthy basis for sexual relationships. This means that he will have no socially acceptable outlet for his sexual drive.

His faith in God will certainly open up the opportunity for change but he will need a lot of help. All too often his spiritual beliefs are bound up with these powerful psychological factors so that he has a dysfunctional faith. The grooming process for targeting his victim has become such an integral part of his thought patterns that he unwittingly uses his faith to disguise or even promote it. This may sound shocking but in fact it is only different in degree from other 'addictive sins' that have less harmful consequences. Many of us have a dysfunctional faith because we are unconsciously using our faith to disguise our faults. Sadly social shame is often more powerful than guilt before God. When Christ said, 'Take up [your] cross and follow me' (Lk 9:23), did he not also mean that each of us would have to 'crucify the old self', in our daily battle with original sin? Herein lies personal responsibility in recognising that there is a sin to be tackled rather than complacently deceiving ourselves and thinking the other person in the wrong. The story of Christ's compassionate handling of the woman taken in adultery is a case in point (Jn 8:3–11).

Beer describes the combination of stern compassion and accountable supervision set out in the Church of England's guidelines: *Meeting the Challenge, How churches should respond to Sex Offenders*. He also introduces the idea of spiritual assessment to help such people whose abnormal psychological drives have become entangled with their belief system producing a dysfunctional faith.

Can bad drive mad?
Does demon possession exist?

Moss (chapter seven) is a Christian psychiatrist with experience in working with pastors in helping people thought to be demonised. He opens up discussion by careful delineation of what demon possession might be and what it is not. This narrows the focus and gives a balanced credible account, neither dismissing it nor attributing a wide range of mental illness to it. He can therefore speak both to practitioners in the Deliverance churches and to sceptical psychiatrists.

Several useful lists help to clarify the definition. These include a scale of severity and vulnerability to demon possession, also entry points and what allows demons to stay, also diagnostic criteria, principles of management and treatment, the indications for and risks of exorcism. People at risk include those who deliberately court evil, seek its power, and delve into the occult. The victims of evil, abused and traumatised people are also vulnerable, so also are the mentally ill whose 'defences are down'.

Demon possession is not synonymous with mental disorder although most of the manifestations can be explained in terms of mental illness. A 'decision tree' is provided to aid differential diagnosis. The first step is to exclude psychotic illness or organic disease of the brain. In that case the belief in demons and the experience of control is delusional and due to disturbed neurochemistry. Nor is a trance state demon possession. Trance states are psycho-physiological phenomena and can be induced by rituals or drugs or result from alteration of consciousness due to dissociation (switching off from intolerable mental pain). Furthermore the assessing therapist must remember that a patient from a traditional culture may simply be expressing his cultural concept of mental illness when saying they are demon possessed. They need an empathic attitude of courtesy and unconditional regard.

The core feature of demon possession seems to be the experience of being taken over by an intrusive alien personality over which the subject has no control and which both they and others see as deviously cunning and manipulative (ie fiendish). However, this description has no 'construct validity', ie the features do not exclusively belong to demon possession but can be explained by mental illness too. Moss quotes research suggesting that Dissociative Identity Disorder (or Multiple Personality Disorder as it used to be called) is associated with a possession syndrome. These people are the severely damaged survivors of childhood abuse described in chapter three. An account of how they can as children pass into dissociative trances and re-enact their abuse is given in chapter two. The 'decision tree' tells how to differentiate between the possession state that arises from such a disturbed personality and what is more likely to be demon possession. If there are strong religious ideas expressed in a very negative manner vilifying the relevant faith in blasphemous terms, demon possession should be considered.

Can we therefore hypothesise that demon possession can only occur if the subject has had some dealings with the occult or become preoccupied with the darker side of the supernatural? Courting evil deliberately seems to be the chief entry point. This means continued indulgence in foul practices, deliberate desecration of what is good, trying to contact the dead, invoking curses from intense malicious hatred, almost 'worshipping' evil. The more a person yields to this the less they will be able to back off. 'Demonic oppression' is reached when normal life is impaired by preoccupation with evil, guilt and fear. Demon possession is envisaged as the end result. A scale of 1–10 for severity of involvement and degree of vulnerability is suggested. Lesser degrees of vulnerability would result from failure to deal with 'emotional garbage', emotional hurts, grievances, hatred, past traumas and unforgiveness etc.

Clearly mental health professionals need to take a 'spiritual history', including occult involvement and what it meant to the patient, if they are to detect such conditions. A sobering thought: is the incidence of occult practice in Western society filling the spiritual gap left by the decline in religious belief? If this were to increase, might we not see more demon possession?

Different faces of bad: the symbolism of demons

As chapter seven develops, demons emerge as a symbol for a dimension of experience that modern Western thought has largely discounted. Moss explores this symbolism. First, belief in demons is a feature of traditional cultures throughout the developing world. It provides a popular explanation for the perplexities of everyday life – illness, crop failure, accident, misfortune, etc. Modern dualism with its emphasis on scientific cause and effect either discounted religion or relegated it to mystical experience. This left no room for a middle zone of folk religion. Belief in ancestors, spirits, saints, charms, etc. all helped to make sense of life. Nevertheless excessive use of this can provide entry points for frank demon possession. This is more likely to occur in cultures in the throes of transition and rapid social change. Immigrants from such cultures who are going through an intensified experience of rapid social change are also vulnerable.

Second, demons as a feature of Christian thought and practice are a way of thinking about the cosmic battle between good and evil being fought out on the battlefield of the individual soul. It is important to uphold the core truth of the life long human vulnerability to evil while keeping an open mind about the actual reality of demons. Demons represent where allegiance lies. For instance we talk about the 'demon alcohol' or 'the god of mammon' referring to the controlling influence of alcohol and wealth.

Bad as top dog: the impact of national evil

Third, consider the impact of determined evil upon the social group, particularly a national society. According to Systems Theory (outlined in chapter two) the beliefs and unwritten rules of the system will shape and dictate the behaviour of the individuals. It is actually very difficult to resist prevailing politically correct ideas. If these are evil then everyone in that society will be affected. In recent history Nazism showed what can happen when a previously civilised and sophisticated society espouses an evil pseudo-religious political ideology. The social dynamic of evil is to empower the bad and scapegoat the weak. Invoking demons and witchcraft distils the evil of the whole of society and focuses it on certain persons. These are either powerful people with a negative charisma or the weak and powerless who become scapegoats for the evil of society. This is more likely to happen in societies with oppressive structures, ineffectual institutions for justice and no hope of change (rigid systems), such as dictatorships. It is sobering to reflect that both Hitler in Nazi Germany and Idi Amin in Uganda were known to consult mediums to guide their policies. The results were disastrous for their populations. This social model of evil might give us a further paradigm for understanding the meaning of the Crucifixion, which seems so puzzling and irrelevant to modern man. If evil scapegoats the weak and empowers the bad how do we understand Christ's sacrifice on the Cross?

He was far from powerless, as he told Pilate, 'You would have no power over me if it were not given to you from above' (Jn 19:11). Yet he deliberately allowed himself to be made a scapegoat. He walked into it on Passover night in fulfilment of prophecy (Luke 22 reports the last Passover meal followed by his arrest). The incarnate God allowed evil to scapegoat himself. Hebrews 10:1–18 describes how Christ became the fulfilment of all the previous sacrifices of atonement. Philippians 2:6–11 sets the scale '…being in very nature God, [he] did not consider equality with God something to be grasped, but made himself nothing, taking the very nature of a servant'. Christ had also to wrestle with the temptation to be empowered by evil during the temptations in the desert (Lk 4:1–13). On both counts he was therefore able to defeat evil: the path of loving sacrifice that he chose was vindicated by the resurrection.

Mad posing as bad:
the internal confusion of traumatised people

The fourth level of symbolism of demons is the psychodynamic interpretation. The field of expertise of the psychotherapist is to understand the working of the inner psychic world of the individual – emotions, instinctive drives, psychological defence mechanisms and unconscious motivations. The aim of the psychotherapist is to get in touch with how the person perceives the world and then guide them through processing (making sense of) traumatic memories. Ghosts, hauntings, demons are seen as isolated fragments of terrifying mental imagery. This is part of the mental life that has evaded synthesis and come to dominate the whole. According to this model, if the belief in demons is not delusional (the person is not psychotic) then it is a defence mechanism. As such it is a way of evading responsibility. The person sees themselves as the passive victim of evil. The belief is an intensified projection of their sense of unacceptable vileness (lust, hate, envy): 'It was not I that did it but the devil in me'. This is the point at which Christian healing operates. The pastoral counsellor puts the emotionally wounded person in touch with the healing power of Christ, which will involve both repentance and forgiveness. He or she may also need a great deal of psychiatric help. This is clearly portrayed in the case history given in chapter seven and further explored in chapter five.

Chapter seven quotes Wilson, an experienced doctor who was both psychotherapist and a pastoral theologian. He viewed 'possession' not so much as relating to demonic involvement, but as a form of 'bondage' cramping the full autonomy of the person who needed help to 'find' themselves and 'love' themselves. The patient was suffering identity confusion because part of their life experience had evaded synthesis and obtained a power of its own to influence and destroy. They must be helped to assume responsibility for it. Wilson used psychotherapy and prayer, always assessing the impact prayer would have upon the patient in terms of their beliefs and suggestibility. The newly integrated person needed upon recovery to belong to a strong normal group (a healthy system). Wilson said, 'A man is a man by reason of other people'.

Banishing bad without wounding mad: exorcism

Chapter seven concludes with a detailed account of the management of the person who regards himself as demon possessed. Moss cautions mental health professionals not to dismiss this belief but to develop an 'emic' (insider's) understanding. Try to empathise with the patient and use the idiom of the culture. Help should be sought from the spiritual leaders of the patient's faith. He cautions the latter that exorcism should only be used as a component of a comprehensive treatment plan after due preparation. He also advises Christian psychiatrists not to attempt two roles but to consult pastors who are experienced in exorcism. Careful clinical and spiritual assessment comes first to identify which of the various factors outlined above apply to the case. For instance social work or legal advocacy may be needed to address abuse or injustice. To perform exorcism without righting flagrant wrongs is to add insult to injury. Psychiatric medication may be needed; for instance if the patient is significantly depressed they will not be in a strong enough frame of mind to take an active part in the exorcism. The latter is very important. Exorcism should only be done with the patient's full knowledge, permission and participation. It is vital that he or she is able to take active responsibility for the 'demonisation' rather than remain in a passive position. It will be a long struggle afterwards. Prior supportive psychotherapy and spiritual counselling enable the patient to stand back and take stock of how they came to this point, to consider different approaches, also the implications for changes in their life and behaviour.

There is a body of research on exorcism. Poor outcome is related to dogmatic and coercive procedures (physical struggles) or long emotional scenes, also to rejection of other causes of distress, exclusion of medical treatment, and failure to address associated social problems and injustice. The worst outcome can lead to deterioration of the patient, dehumanisation, despair, helplessness, and a feeling of having been emotionally manipulated and misunderstood. In the right setting wisely handled exorcism can liberate the patient and set them on course for recovery. Young people who have been extensively harmed will need much rebuilding of their lives.

Finally, Moss warns that exorcism must occur with the backing and support of a strong normal church fellowship and must lead to a relationship with Christ. Moreover, those who practise exorcism expose themselves to the power of evil, the temptation to wield power over others. They will need the constraints of the group, that is the church, to maintain humility and a God-fearing attitude, lest they get sucked in. The power of evil is a force to be reckoned with.

Outwitting bad to cure mad: spiritual healing

Spiritual healing as an additional way of helping the mentally disturbed is a tentative conclusion of this book. What form should it take? The most difficult category for the psychiatrist to treat is personality disorder. These people all too often were damaged in early childhood by the folly of others. How can that legacy be dealt with? Justice in the courts does not resolve the psychological impact. Psychoanalysis seeks to explore the inner psychic world and help the person understand what has happened to them. But when it has all been brought to light what do they do with it? They still have to live with that sense of having been wronged – or of having done wrong. This is where a spiritual dimension is necessary.

The first step in any healing is to engage the patient in the idea that there is a problem to be treated. Too often there is denial or evasion or complacency. If they do not see any need, it is impossible to treat them – without recourse to the Mental Health Act. Indeed the process of engagement is the beginning of healing. Thinking it through, admitting to themselves that action needs to be taken, all paves the way for recovery. Repentance is similar to engagement. Most people do not find it easy to apologise; but there is no doubt that doing so restores relationships wonderfully. Repentance before God is similar – humiliating and abasing initially, but marvellous for the peace of mind afterwards.

Forgiveness does not feature much in psychiatry. Yet, as we have seen, 'mad' can be inextricably entangled with 'bad'. The rite of confession not long ago held a key place in our culture as a means of resolving personal difficulties, living harmoniously with others and achieving peace of mind. Maybe it became too glib but it has been superseded by the politically correct idea that psychological counselling is the answer.

In Christian pastoral counselling forgiveness, and its precursor repentance, holds a vital place in 'inner healing' (chapter five). People who have been harmed by the abuse of others especially if it was 'Significant Harm', a legal term from the Children Act denoting harm to the child's development from inadequate parental care, often carry a huge burden of bitterness, anger and hate. In many respects this seems justified – yet the burden is poisoning them. How can they be freed of it? Forgiveness in inner healing is not simply expecting the victim to forgive the perpetrator. That would beg the question of responsibility. It is primarily asking God's forgiveness for the bitterness and hate in the heart. The sufferer delegates to God the business of dealing with the abuser. 'Vengeance is mine saith the Lord' (see Na 1:2–3; Ps 94:1). As their counselling progresses they may be more able through the grace of Christ to forgive those who harmed them. This will further heal them. This concept is further developed in the Sandfords' book, *The Transformation of the Inner Man.*[3]

Nailing bad for good: God's solution

This gives us a further paradigm of the Crucifixion. It may seem to the victim an enormity to say that he needs forgiveness for his anger and bitterness against the perpetrator in order to achieve peace of mind. Yet to be relieved of that burden would indeed be therapeutic. Even more so is the relief of remorse for the aggressor. Christian forgiveness is very different from other views of forgiveness. On the one hand the Cross seems irrelevant to modern life. On the other hand to forgive atrocities seems a mountainous impossibility, let alone actually to repent to God of the just feeling of anger.

The pastoral counsellor helps the wronged and traumatised person to understand the scale of the Incarnation and what God did in allowing himself to become a victim. This spiritual counselling is conducted in the context of a psychotherapeutic approach exploring the patient's experience with unconditional positive regard and a non-judgmental attitude. The Messiah was the Suffering Servant (Is 53) who was both the High Priest and the sacrifice (Heb 4:14–5:10). In Christ God became human and was therefore able to sympathise with our weaknesses. Yet Jesus also revealed God as uncompromisingly righteous. Bad was to have no leeway at all and certainly not to destroy those whom God loved. Jesus told a story to illustrate this. He is like a shepherd searching for one lost sheep, even though he already has 99 safe in the fold. He allowed himself to suffer an enormity of humiliation, rejection and abuse to achieve this. The patient can identify with the paradox of the Servant King. He did indeed become the projection of all our sins and sufferings; he took them upon himself.

No foothold for mad: the need for social morality

Prevention is better than cure especially with incurable, though not untreatable, conditions such as personality disorder. Chapter two outlines the recent research on imprinting upon the infant brain. This shows the vital importance of the first years of life when the brain is actually programmed and the foundations of the personality are laid. 'The hand that rocks the cradle rules the world'.[4] Crime prevention needs to start in the cradle.

The mother–infant relationship is the crucial factor yet it is one of the most vulnerable and defenceless of human relationships. The role of the family, particularly the father, is to protect it. Chapter two outlines how the integrity of family life is strongly influenced by the prevailing social mores. Breakdown in the social fabric of society first affects the most vulnerable and thereby the mental health of the developing children. Sexual morality is not simply about the behaviour of adults. It is about safeguarding the human

ecosystem for rearing the next generation, ie the biological purpose
of sex including the resulting parental responsibility.

It is interesting to read the old marriage service in the *Church
of England Book of Common Prayer* (1548). 'Marriage was ordained
for the procreation of children, that they may be brought up in the
fear and nurture of the Lord…secondly to satisfy man's carnal lusts
and as a remedy against sin…thirdly for the mutual society, help
and comfort the one ought to have of the other.' This sounds archaic
nowadays but it formed the basis for social morality for centuries.
It is sobering to reflect that it was written by men who were
later burnt at the stake – Cranmer, Latimer and Ridley. Latimer's
exhortation is well known: 'Be of good comfort, Master Ridley, and
play the man. We shall this day light such a candle by God's grace
in England, as shall never be put out'. These brave men did not die
simply to uphold marriage but for their belief in the reformation of
the values that kept society wholesome. Those same values, which
have been the foundation of our culture, are now being wantonly
abandoned.

This discussion begs the question of whether there is an
absolute morality and how it is ordained and upheld. All intact
cultures and religious faiths have a moral structure for safeguarding
family life and rearing and socialising the next generation. Western
culture can no longer be said to be intact. It is changing so fast under
various complex influences. Moreover, it is subject to the massive
but unquantified and unregulated impact of the media. The Church
of England, through the Lichfield Diocesan Synod, has proposed a
motion that the Government examine *the erosion in the standards of
behaviour from the media's exploitation of other human beings.* Several
bishops have supported this motion, concerned that: 'Television
programmes tend to push the boundaries in the battle for ratings.
The threshold of what is acceptable for sex and violence continues
to be challenged and it changes the view of society. Under-age
sex, teenage violence, loss of respect on the street, the bullying
culture, even the increase in gun crime, could reflect images and
values portrayed on television which is the daily cultural diet of
most children. The last half century has seen a massive experiment
carried out by bombarding people, particularly the young, with
images they have never been subjected to before. We need to look
at the results of that experiment'.[5]

The contributors to this book would certainly support such
an enquiry. The conclusion of this mad/bad debate is that social
morality has an important shaping effect on mental health.

There is a body of research on the impact of screen violence.[6] Young people who have grown up experiencing domestic violence, seeing father beat up mother, being beaten themselves, learning that 'those who love you most also hit you most' are at risk of committing violent offences. They are also drawn to and are fascinated by screen violence. Watching violent films reinforces violent behaviour and increases the chance of acting it out (partly through dissociative flashbacks of their own terrifying experiences). This is so of only a small number of high profile youths, but they are the ones who commit the seemingly meaningless violent crimes. The normal population of young people who have had 'good enough parenting' (a technical term coined by Winnicott – see chapter two) can become inured to violence by watching it repeatedly on screen, but they do not seem to act it out. They can become 'bystanders, they just walk by on the other side' instead of being shocked by it. It behoves responsible parents to protect their young children from the media. Research into other types of impact, such as how much the media influences our cultural beliefs and social safeguards, would have to be a sophisticated study as such things are not easy to measure.

Those naughty jesters bad and mad: conclusion to a false dichotomy

This analysis of the interface between religious faith and mental ill health has shown a false dichotomy. The psychological and spiritual dimensions are intricately intertwined. Indeed elucidating one illuminates the other. The Bible, which is our source of information on God's relationship with us, seems to blend the two dimensions harmoniously. Jesus had a profound understanding of the psychology of those he dealt with, as is shown repeatedly in the Gospel narratives: the woman at the well (Jn 4:4–26); the woman taken in adultery (Jn 8:1–11); the call of Matthew (Mt 9:9–13); his response to the faithful centurion (Lk 7:1–10); his advice to Mary and Martha (Lk 10:38–42); his searching restoration of Peter to be the disciples' leader after his betrayal (Jn 21:15–19); his many dealings with the Pharisees and the subtlety of his parables. He used psychological insights to teach spiritual truths. Paul's Epistles to the early church also contain much sound advice on how to resolve difficulties in relationships (eg Gal 6:1–5).

The more psychological insights are brought to bear, the more we can understand spiritual issues and vice versa. The dual understanding throws things into three dimensions. They are not, however, the same. One important distinction is the place of morality. Whereas the psychological approach avoids judgments of right and wrong, the spiritual perspective sees moral issues as inescapable. This is because matters of right and wrong determine how the spiritual part develops. It seems that in mental health 'mad' and 'bad' are inextricably interwoven.

Index

Y

References, questions for discussion and further reading

Chapter 1: What is mental disorder? by Andrew C P Sims

References

1   Zilboorg G, Henry GW. *A History of Medical Psychology.* New York: WW Norton, 1941.
2   Cohn N. *Europe's Inner Demons.* London: Sussex University Press, 1975.
3   Dominian J. *One Like Us: A Psychological Interpretation of Jesus.* London: Darton, Longman & Todd, 1998.
4   World Health Organization. *ICD-10 Classification of Mental and Behavioural Disorders.* Geneva: World Health Organization, 1992.
5   Sedgwick P. Illness – mental and otherwise. In Caplan AL, Engelhardt HT, McCartney JJ. *Concepts of Health and Disease: Interdisciplinary Perspectives.* London: Addison-Wesley, 1981.
6   Bluglass R, Bowden P. *Principles and Practice of Forensic Psychiatry.* Edinburgh: Churchill Livingstone, 1990.
7   World Health Organization. Constitution of the World Health Organization. *Official Record of the World Health Questionnaire* 1946;2:100.
8   Kendell RE. The distinction between mental and physical illness. *British Journal of Psychiatry* 2001;178:490–493.
9   Sims ACP. *Personality disorder.* In Gregory RL. *The Oxford Companion to the Mind (2nd Edition).* Oxford: Oxford University Press, 2004.
10 Livesley WJ. *Handbook of Personality Disorders: Theory, Research and Treatment.* New York: Guilford, 2001.
11 Larson DB, Pattison EM, Blazer DG, Omran AR, Kaplan BH. Systematic analysis of research on religious variables in four major psychiatric journals, 1978–1982. *American Journal of Psychiatry* 1986;143:329–334.

Questions for discussion

1. Is it helpful or possible to impute psychiatric diagnoses to biblical characters?
2. How did the distinction arise in the Church that the physically ill were unfortunate but the mentally ill sinful?
3. For which biblical characters and stories is it useful to look at our modern understanding of psychological and family dynamics?
4. Does the concept of dissocial personality disorder rightly belong with theology or psychiatry?
5. What are appropriate responses of people in churches to the mentally ill and their problems?
6. How should people in churches view the management of those with severe personality disorder?

Further reading
See those listed in references for chapter one above, especially Dominian,
    Gregory and Livesley, and also:
Davies G. *Stress: The Challenge to Christian Caring.* Eastbourne: Kingsway
    Publications, 1988.
Davies G. *Genius, Grief and Grace: A Doctor Looks at Suffering and Success.* Location:
    Geanies House/Christian Focus Publications, 2001.
Gelder M, López-Ibor JJ, Andreasen NC. *New Oxford Textbook of Psychiatry,*
    Oxford: Oxford University Press, 2000.
Sims A. *Symptoms in the Mind (3rd Edition).* Edinburgh: Elsevier, 2002.
Whybrow PC. *A Mood Apart: Depression, Mania and other Afflictions of the Self.*
    New York: Basic Books, 1997.
Wing JK. *Reasoning about Madness.* Oxford: Oxford University Press, 1978.

Chapter 2: Childhood influences on antisocial behaviour, by Elizabeth A Guinness

References
1   Rutter M *et al.* Genetics and child psychiatry: II. Empirical research
    findings. *Journal of Child Psychology and Psychiatry* 1999;40:19–56.
2   Bentovim A, Gorell-Barnes G, Cooklin A (eds). *Family Therapy.* New
    York: Institute of Family Therapy, Academic Press (Grune & Stratton),
    1982.
3   West DJ, Farrington DP. *Who becomes delinquent?* London: Heineman,
    Educational, 1973.
4   Miller FJW *et al.* Becoming deprived: a cross-generational study based
    on the Newcastle 1000 Family Study. In Nicol AR (ed). *Longitudinal
    Studies in Child Psychology and Psychiatry.* Chichester: Wiley, 1988.
5   Bailey A *et al.* Autism as a strongly genetic disorder; Evidence from a
    British Twin Study. *Psychological Medicine* 1995;25:63–77.
6   Kendler KS. Major depression and generalised anxiety disorder:
    same genes, different environments. *British Journal of Psychiatry*
    1996;168(suppl. 30):68–75.
7   Biederman J *et al.* Further evidence for familial genetic risk factors in
    ADHD: patterns of comorbidity in probands and relatives in psychiatrically
    and paediatrically referred samples. *Archives of General Psychiatry*
    1992;49:728–738; Goodman R, Stevenson J. A twin study of hyperactivity. II:
    The aetiological role of genes, family relationships and perinatal adversity.
    Journal of Child Psychology and Psychiatry 1989;30:691–709.
8   Gillberg C. Autism and autistic like conditions: subclasses among
    disorders of empathy. *Journal of Child Psychology & Psychiatry*
    1992;33:813–842.
9   Rutter M. Family and school influences on cognitive development.
    Journal of Child Psychology and Psychiatry 1985;26:683–704.
10 Glaser D. Child Abuse and Neglect and the Brain – A Review. *Journal of
    Child Psychology and Psychiatry* 2000;41:97–116.
11 Besharov DJ. Headstart: Making a popular program work. *Paediatrics*
    1987;79(3):440–444.
12 Garber H, Herber R. Modification of predicted cognitive development
    in high risk children through early intervention. In Detterman MK,
    Sternberg RJ (eds). *How and How Much can Intelligence be Increased?*
    Norwood, New Jersey: Ablex Publishing Co, 1982:121–137.

13   Kanner L. Autistic disturbance of affective contact. *Nervous Child.* 1943;2:217–250.

14   Fombonne E. The Epidemiology of Autism: a review. *Psychological Medicine* 1999;29:769–786.

15   Bailey A, Phillips W, Rutter M. Autism: Towards an integration of clinical genetic and neuropsychological and neurobiological perspectives. *Journal of Child Psychology & Psychiatry* 1996;37:51–88.

16   Zahn-Waxler C. Development of concern for others. *Developmental Psychology* 1992;28:126–136.

17   Done DJ *et al*. Childhood antecedents of schizophrenia and affective illness: social adjustment at age 7 and 11. *BMJ* 1994;309:699–703.

18   Gillberg C, Wing L. Autism: not an extremely rare disorder. *Acta Scandinavica Psychiatrica* 1999;99:399–406.

19   Pennington BF, Ozonoff S. Executive function and developmental psychopathology. *Journal of Child Psychology & Psychiatry* 1996;37:51–58.

20   Barkley R. *ADHD, A Handbook of Diagnosis and Treatment*. New York: Guildford Press, 1990.

21   Satterfield JH, Hoppe CM, Schell AM. A prospective study of delinquency in 110 adolescent boys with ADHD and 88 normal boys. *American Journal of Psychiatry* 1982;139:795–798; Weiss G *et al*. Psychiatric status of hyperactives as adults: a controlled prospective 15 yr follow up of 63 hyperactive children. *Journal of the American Academy of Child & Adolescent Psychiatry* 1985;24:211–220; Rutter *et al*, 1999 (see ref. 1); Lynam DR. Early identification of chronic offenders: Who is the fledgling psychopath? *Psychological Bulletin* 1996;120:209–234.

22   Brown TE (ed). *Attention Deficit Disorders and Comorbidity in Children, Adolescents and Adults*. Washington DC: American Psychiatric Press, 2000.

23   Robins L. Sturdy childhood predictors of adult antisocial behaviour: Replication of longitudinal studies. *Psychological Medicine* 1978;8:611–622; Taylor E *et al*. *The epidemiology of childhood hyperactivity. Maudsley Monographs. No. 33*. Oxford: Oxford University Press, 1991.

24   Bohman M. Predisposition to criminality. Swedish adoption studies in retrospect. In Bock GR, Goode JA (eds). Genetics of Criminal and Antisocial Behaviour. *Ciba Symposium* 1996;194:99–114.

25   Scott S *et al*. Multicentre controlled trial of parenting groups for childhood antisocial behaviour in clinical practice. *BMJ* 2001a;323:194–198; Scott S *et al*. Financial cost of social exclusion: follow up study of antisocial children into adulthood. *BMJ* 2001b;323:191.

26   Thomas A *et al*. Temperament and follow up to adulthood. In Porter R, Collins GM (eds). *Temperamental differences in infants and young children*. London: Pitman, 1982:168–172.

27   Lynam, 1996 (see ref. 21).

28   Eisenberg N, Lennon R. Sex differences in empathy and related capacities. *Psychological Bulletin* 1983;94:100–131.

29   Whiting BB. The genesis of prosocial behaviour. In Bridgeman D (ed). *The Nature of Prosocial Development: Interdisciplinary theories and strategies*. London: Academic Press, 1983.

30   Zahn-Waxler C. Warriors and worriers: Gender and psychopathology. *Development and Psychopathology* 1993;5:79–89.

31   Phillips ML. An investigation of facial recognition, memory and happy and sad facial expression perception. An fMRI study. *Psychiatry Research* 1998;83(3):127–138.

32   Skuse D *et al*. Evidence from Turner's syndrome of an imprinted

X-linked locus affecting cognitive function. *Nature* 1997;387:705–708.

33   Woodruff RA, Robins LN, Winokur G, Reich T. Manic depressive illness and social achievement. *Acta Psychiatrica Scandinavica* 1971;47:237–249.

34   Biederman J *et al*. ADHD and Juvenile Mania: an overlooked comorbidity? *Journal of the American Academy of Child & Adolescent Psychiatry* 1996;4:997–1008.

35   See George Brown's classic work. (Brown GW, Harris T. *The Social Origins of Depression*. London: Tavistock, 1978.)

36   Yusuf S *et al*. Global burden of cardiovascular diseases: part II variations in cardiovascular disease by specific ethnic groups and geographic regions and preventive strategies. *Circulation* 2001;104:2855–2864.

37   Erikson EH. *Childhood and Society*. Norton: New York, 1950.

38   Piaget J. *The Child's Construction of Reality (translation by M Cook)*. London: Routledge & Kegan Paul, 1955. (Original French edition 1937.)

39   Winnicott DW. *The maturational process and facilitating environment*. London: Hogarth Press, 1965.

40   Bowlby J. *Attachment and Loss*. London: Hogarth Press, 1969.

41   Johnson Z *et al*. Community mothers programme: randomised controlled trial of non-professional intervention in parenting. *BMJ* 1993;306:1449–1452.

42   Rutter M *et al*. Quasi-autistic patterns following severe early global deprivation. *Journal of Child Psychology and Psychiatry* 1999a;40:537–550.

43   Rutter M *et al*. Developmental catch-up and deficit following adoption after severe global early deprivation. *Journal of Child Psychology and Psychiatry* 1998;39:465–476.

44   Greenough W, Black J. Induction of Brain Structure by Experience: substrate for cognitive development. In Gunnar MR, Nelson CA (eds). *Minnesota Symposia on Child Psychology*. Hillsdale NJ: Lawrence Erlbaum, 1992:155–200.

45   Davidson R. Asymmetric brain function, affective style and psychopathology: The role of early experience and plasticity. *Development and Psychopathology* 1994;6:741–758.

46   Dawson G *et al*. Infants of depressed mothers exhibit atypical frontal brain activity: a replication and extension of previous findings. *Journal of Child Psychology & Psychiatry* 1997;38:179–186.

47   Van Der Kolk B, Fisler R. Childhood abuse and neglect and loss of self regulation. *Bulletin of the Menninger Clinic* 1994;58:145–168.

48   Cummings EM, Davies PT. Maternal depression and child development. *Journal of Child Psychology & Psychiatry* 1994;35:73–112; Hay DF *et al*. Intellectual problems shown by 11 year old children whose mothers had post natal depression. *Journal of Child Psychology and Psychiatry* 2001;42:871–889.

49   Gunnar M. Quality of early care and buffering of neuroendocrine stress reactions: Potential effects on the developing human brain. *Preventive Medicine* 1998;27:208–211.

50   McLanahan S, Sandefur G. *Growing up with a single parent: What hurts, what helps*. Cambridge, MA: Harvard University Press, 1994; Weiss RS. *Going it alone: the family life and social situation of the single parent*. New York: Basic Books, 1979.

51   Belsky J. Developmental Risks still associated with Early Child Care. *Journal of Psychology and Psychiatry* 2001;42:845–859.

52   Quinton D, Rutter M. Parenting behaviour of mothers raised in care. In Nicol AR (ed). *Longitudinal Studies in Child Psychology & Psychiatry*. Chichester: Wiley, 1985:157–201.

53 Skuse D, Bentovim A, Hodges J. Risk factors for the development of sexually abusive behaviour in sexually victimised adolescent boys: cross sectional study. *BMJ* 1998;317:175–179.

54 Stevenson J. The treatment of the long term *sequelae* of child sexual abuse. *Journal of Child Psychology & Psychiatry*. 1999;40:89–112.

55 Rutter M *et al*. Attainment and adjustment in two geographical areas. I. Prevalence of Psychiatric Disorders. *British Journal of Psychiatry* 1975;126:493–509; Goodman R. UK National Statistics Office, 2000.

56 Power C. A review of child health in the 1958 birth cohort: National Child Development study. *Paediatric & Perinatal Epidemiology* 1992;6(1):81–110.

57 See Rutter's elegant study. (Rutter M *et al*. *Fifteen thousand hours: Secondary schools and their effects on children*. London: Open Books, 1979.)

58 Guinness EA. Profile and prevalence of the brain fag syndrome: psychiatric morbidity in school populations in Africa. *British Journal of Psychiatry* 1992;160(suppl.16):42–52.

59 Hetherington EM, Stanley Hagain M. Adjustment of children with divorced parents: A risk and resiliency perspective. *Journal of Child Psychology & Psychiatry* 1999;40:129–140.

60 Amato PR, Keith B. Parent Divorce and the well being of children. *Psychological Bulletin* 1991;110(1):26–46.

61 Lambert R, Streather J. *Children in changing families: a study in adoption and illegitimacy*. London: Macmillan Press, 1980.

62 Guinness E. Brief reactive psychosis and the major psychoses: descriptive case studies in Africa. *British Journal of Psychiatry* 1992;160(suppl.16):24–41.

63 See Young Minds *www.youngminds.org.uk/sos* (2006).

64 See Scott S *et al*. *www.iop.kcl.ac.uk/iopweb/departments/home/default. aspx?locator=394*

65 Guinness E. Social origins of the brain fag syndrome. Patterns of mental illness in the early stages of urbanization. *British Journal of Psychiatry* 1992;160(suppl.16):53–64.

66 McGuire J, Earls F. Prevention of child psychiatric disorders in early childhood. *Journal of Child Psychology and Psychiatry* 1991;32:129–154.

67 Nicol R. *Helping mothers and toddlers in the inner city: a controlled trial of 3 approaches*. Paper presented at the Annual Conference of the Association of Child Psychology and Psychiatry, London, July 1987.

Questions for discussion

For mental health and social work professionals:

1. What are the implications of imprinting research for adoption and fostering policies?

2. What should be the active multidisciplinary management policy for maternal depression in terms of adult psychiatry teams and under fives' child mental health teams?

3. What action can be taken by local communities (initiated by a combination of statutory professions, voluntary groups and church leaders) on the following:
    a) in making a systemic diagnosis of the community and identifying local social evils?
    b) facilitating the progress through adolescence of local young people?
    c) identifying and supporting local community initiatives?

For church fellowships:
1. What is the nature of sin in psychological terms in the light of this child development analysis?
2. How does a healthy spiritual faith enable a person to overcome his/her innate weaknesses?
3. How can a person change a 'neurotic relationship with God' to a more healthy faith?
4. How do the dynamics of the church as a social group facilitate and empower its members?
5. How can the media be monitored, managed and used constructively for the good of the people?

Chapter 3: Treatment approaches for those with antisocial personality disorders, psychopathy and for sex offenders, by M Dominic Beer

References
1   Jaspers K. *General Psychopathology (translated from German, 7th Edition of 1959 by M. Hamilton, 1st Edition Published 1913).* Manchester: Manchester University Press, 1963.
2   Schneider K. *Clinical Psychopathology (translated by MW Hamilton from the German 5th edition, 1958).* New York and London: Grune and Stratton, 1959.
3   World Health Organisation (WHO). *International Classification of Diseases 10.* Geneva: WHO, 1992.
4   Kendell RE. The distinction between personality disorder and mental illness. *British Journal of Psychiatry* 2002;180:110–115.
5   American Psychiatric Association (APA). *Diagnostic and Statistical Manual of Mental Disorders (4th edition) (DSM-IV).* Washington DC: APA, 1994.
6   Coid JW. Aetiological risk factors for personality disorders. *British Journal of Psychiatry* 1999;174:530–538.
7   Wing L. Asperger's Syndrome: A clinical account. *Psychological Medicine* 1981;11:115–129.
8   Coid JW. Epidemiology, public health and the problem of personality disorder. *British Journal of Psychiatry* 2003;182(suppl. 44):S3–S10.
9   Winston AP. Recent developments in borderline personality disorder. *Advances in Psychiatric Treatment* 2000;6:211–218.
10 Moran P. *Antisocial personality disorder. An Epidemiological Perspective.* London: Gaskell and The Royal College of Psychiatrists, 1999:74.
11 Farrington DP. The challenge of teenage antisocial behaviour. In Rutter M (ed). *Psychosocial Disturbances in Young People, Challenges for Prevention.* Cambridge: Cambridge University Press, 1995:83–130.
12 Rutter M (ed). *Psychosocial Disturbances in Young People, Challenges for Prevention.* Cambridge: Cambridge University Press, 1995:xi–xii.
13 Hart SD, Hare RD. Psychopathy and risk assessment. *Current Opinion in Psychiatry* 1996;9:380–383.
14 Hart SD, Hare RD. Psychopathy and antisocial personality disorder. *Current Opinion in Psychiatry* 1996;9:129–132.
15 Sims A. *Symptoms in the Mind. An Introduction to Descriptive Psychopathology (3rd edition).* London: Saunders, 2003:383.

16 Blair RJR. Neurobiological basis of psychopathy. *British Journal of Psychiatry* 2003;182:5–7.

17 Coid JW. Current concepts and classifications of psychopathic disorder in personality disorder reviewed. In Tyrer P, Stein G (eds). *Personality Disorder Reviewed*. London: Gaskell and Royal College of Psychiatrists, 1993:113–164.

18 Quoted in Moran, 1999 (see ref. 10).

19 Peck MS. *People of the Lie*. London: Arrow Books, 1990.

20 American Psychiatric Association (APA). *Diagnostic and Statistical Manual of Mental Disorders (DSM-IV) (4th edition)*. Washington DC: APA, 1994

21 Peck, 1990 (see ref. 19, pp.154–155).

22 Peck, 1990 (see ref. 19, p.77).

23 Peck, 1990 (see ref. 19, p.82).

24 Peck, 1990 (see ref. 19, p.91).

25 Vann G. *The Pain of Christ and the Sorrow of God*. New York: Alba House, 1994. Quoted by Peck, 1990 (see ref. 19, p.81).

26 Morse SJ. Craziness and criminal responsibility. *Behav Sci Law* 1999;17:147–164. Quoted in Wilson S, Adshead G. Criminal Responsibility. In Radden J (ed). *The Philosophy of Psychiatry: a Companion*. New York: Oxford University Press, 2004.

27 Barkan E. *The guilt of nations: Restitution and negotiating historical injustices*. New York & London: W.W. Norton & Company, 2000.

28 Zehr H. *The Little Book of Restorative Justice*. Pennsylvania: Good Books, 2002.

29 Green CM, Naismith LJ, Menzies RD. Criminal responsibility and mental disorder in Britain and North America: A comparative study. *Med Sci Law* 1991;31:45–54.

30 Felthous AR. Introduction to mental illness and criminal responsibility. *Behav Sciences and the Law* 1999;17:143–146.

31 Hart HLA. *Punishment and responsibility: essays in the philosophy of law*. Oxford: Clarendon Press, 1968. Quoted in Wilson S, Adshead G, 2004. (see ref. 26).

32 Griew E. Reducing murder to manslaughter: Whose job? *Journal of Medical Ethics* 1986;12:18–23.

33 Sims, 2003 (see ref. 15, pp.350–351).

34 Sims, 2003 (see ref. 15, p.351).

35 Gelder M, Gath D, Mayou R. *Oxford Textbook of Psychiatry (2nd edition)*. Oxford: Oxford University Press, 1989.

36 Mullen P. Dangerous people with severe personality disorder. *BMJ* 1999;319:1146–1147.

37 Eastman N. Who should take responsibility for antisocial personality disorder? *BMJ* 1999a;318:206–207; Eastman N. Public health psychiatry or crime prevention? *BMJ* 1999b;318:549–551; Eastman N. *Ethics and new mental health legislation. Personality Disorder and Human Worth*. London: Church of England:7-12.

38 Hill J. Early identification of individuals at risk for antisocial personality disorder. *British Journal of Psychiatry* 2003;182(suppl.44):S11–S14; Rutter M, Cox A, Tupling C *et al*. Attainment and adjustment in two geographical areas. 1: The prevalence of psychiatric disorder. *British Journal of Psychiatry* 1975;126:493–509.

39   Coid JW. Formulating strategies for the primary prevention of adult
      antisocial behaviour: 'High risk' or 'population' strategies? In Farrington
      DP, Coid JW (eds). *Early Prevention of Adult Antisocial Behaviour.*
      Cambridge: Cambridge University Press, 2003:32–78.

40   Tremblay RE, Japel C. Prevention during pregnancy, infancy and the
      pre-school years. In Farrington DP, Coid JW (eds). *Early Prevention of
      Adult Antisocial Behaviour.* Cambridge: Cambridge University Press,
      2003:205–242.

41   Utting D. Prevention through family and parenting programmes.
      In Farrington DP, Coid JW (eds). *Early Prevention of Adult Antisocial
      Behaviour.* Cambridge: Cambridge University Press, 2003:243–264.

42   Hawkins JD, Herrenkohl T. Prevention in the school years. In Farrington
      DP, Coid JW (eds). *Early Prevention of Adult Antisocial Behaviour*.
      Cambridge: Cambridge University Press, 2003.

43   Wallace R, Wallace D. Socio-economic determinants of health:
      Community marginalisation and the diffusion of disease and disorder in
      the United States. *BMJ* 1997;314:1341–1345.

44   Rutter M, Smith DJ (eds). *Psychosocial Disorders in Young People*. London:
      Wiley, 1995.

45   Home Office and Department of Health. *Managing dangerous people
      with severe personality disorder. Proposals for policy development.* London:
      Department of Health, 1999.

46   Coid JW, Maden T. Should psychiatrists protect the public? A new risk
      reduction strategy supporting criminal justice could be effective. *BMJ*
      2003;326:406–407.

47   Adshead G. Murmurs of discontent: Treatment and treatability of
      personality disorder. *Advances in Psychiatric Treatment* 2001;7:407–415.

48   Adshead, 2001 (see ref. 47).

49   Tyrer P. Commentary on murmurs of discontent: treatment and
      treatability of personality disorder. *Advances in Psychiatric Treatment*
      2000;7:415–416.

50   Quoted by Tyrer, 2000 (see ref. 49).

51   Adshead, 2001 (see ref. 47, p.411).

52   Bateman A, Fonagy P. The effectiveness of partial hospitalisation in the
      treatment of borderline personality disorder – a randomised controlled
      trial. *American Journal of Psychiatry* 1999;156:1563–1568; Dolan BM,
      Warren FM, Menzies D *et al*. Cost effect following specialist treatment
      of severe personality disorders. *Psychiatric Bulletin* 1996;20:413–417.

53   Johnson R. Modern day lepers. In *Personality Disorder and Human
      Worth*. Papers from a conference organised by the Board for Social
      Responsibility, Church House, London. London: Church of England,
      2001.

54   Johnson, 2001 (see ref. 53, p.18).

55   Johnson, 2001 (see ref. 53, p.20).

56   Johnson, 2001 (see ref. 53, pp.18–19).

57   Johnson, 2001 (see ref. 53, p.20).

58   Pullinger J. *Chasing the Dragon*. London: Hodder and Stoughton, 2001.

59   Williams SB. *A journey towards wholeness in a Christian therapeutic
      community.* Unpublished MPhil Thesis: University of Birmingham, 2003.

60   Newell T. Treating the untreatable? In *Personality Disorder and
      Human Worth. Papers from a conference organised by the Board for Social
      Responsibility.* London: Church of England, 2001:21–27.

61   See Newell, 2001 (ref. 60, p.24).

62   Craissati *et al.* In NIMHE, 2003 (see ref. 67, pp.26–27). For further details see Craissati J, Horne L, Taylor R. *Effective treatment models for personality disordered offenders*, 2002. *www.doh.uk.*

63   Andrews G, Jenkins R (eds). *Management of Mental Disorders. (UK edition). Volume 2.* Sydney: World Health Organization Collaborating Centre for Mental Health and Substance Abuse, 1999:645–646.

64   Warren F, Preedy K, McCauley G, Pickering A *et al. Review of treatments for dangerous and severe personality disorder. Draft Report.* London: Home Office, 2001.

65   Dolan BM, Coid JW. *Psychopathic and antisocial personality disorders. Treatment and research issues.* London: Gaskell and Royal College of Psychiatrists, 1993:277–293.

66   Castillo H. *Personality disorder. Temperament or trauma?* London & Philadelphia: Jessica Kingsley Publishers, 2003.

67   National Institute for Mental Health in England (NIMHE). *Personality Disorder: No Longer a Diagnosis of Exclusion. Policy Implementation Guidance for the Development of Services for People with Personality Disorder.* London: NIMHE, 2003:22.

68   American Psychiatric Association. Practice Guideline for the Treatment of Patients with Borderline Personality Disorder. *American Journal of Psychiatry* 2001;158(suppl.10):1–52.

69   Dolan BM, Warren F, Norton K. Change in borderline symptoms one year after therapeutic community treatment for severe personality disorder. *British Journal of Psychiatry* 1997;171:274–279.

70   Bateman, Fonagy, 1999 (see ref. 52); Bateman A, Fonagy P. Treatment of borderline personality with psychoanalytically oriented partial hospitalization: an 18-month follow-up. *American Journal of Psychiatry* 2001;158:36–42.

71   Craissati J. *Child sexual abusers. A community treatment approach.* Hove: Psychology Press, 1998.

72   Finkelhor D. *Child Sexual Abuse.* New York: The Free Press, 1984.

73   Craissati, 1998 (see ref. 71, p.60).

74   Craissati, 1998 (see ref. 71, p.62).

75   Churches Together in Britain and Ireland. *Time for action – Sexual abuse, the churches and a new dawn for survivors.* London: Churches Together in Britain and Ireland, 2002.

76   Board of Responsibility of the Church of England. *Meeting the Challenge. How churches should respond to sex offenders.* London: Church of England, 1999:102.

77   Malony HN (ed). *Wholeness and Holiness.* Grand Rapids: Baker Book House, 1983; Malony HN. Assessing religious maturity. In Stern EM (ed). *Psychotherapy and the Religiously Committed Patient.* New York: Haworth Press, 1985:25–33; Malony HN. DOGMAT(IC) Pastoral Counselling. *Journal of Pastoral Counselling* 1987;22:89–97; Malony HN. The clinical assessment of optimal religious functioning. *Review of Religious Research* 1988;30:1,3–17; Malony HN. Religious diagnosis in evaluations of mental health. In Schumaker JF (ed). *Religion and Mental Health.* New York and Oxford: Oxford University Press, 1992:247–258; Malony HN. Theological functioning and mental health. In Demarinis, Wickstrom (eds). *The Clinical Assessment of Religion.* Uppsala: University of Uppsala, 1994:1–8 (author's proof copy).

78   Hall T. The spiritual effects of childhood sexual abuse. *Journal of Psychology and Theology* 1995;23(2):129–134.
79   *Guidance to Churches: Protecting Children and Appointing Children's Workers.* PO Box 133, Swanley, Kent BR8 7UQ: Churches' Child Protection Advisory Service, PCCA Christian Child Care, 1998.

Chapter 4: Responsibility and the mentally ill offender, by M Dominic Beer and Janet M Parrott

References
1   Quoted in Reznek L. *Evil or Ill? Justifying the Insanity Defence.* London: Routledge, 1993.
2   American Penal Code, 1962 (Section 2.02(2)).
3   R v McNaughton, 1843.
4   Bratty v Attorney General for Northern Ireland, 1963.
5   HM Advocate v Dingwall, 1867.
6   HM Advocate v Savage, 1923.
7   Smith JC, Hogan B. *Criminal Law (9th edition).* London: Butterworths, 1999.
8   Atkinson D. *Pastoral Ethics.* Oxford: Lynx Communications, 1994.
9   Williams RC. *A Condition of Complete Simplicity – Franciscan Wisdom for Everyday Living.* Norwich: Canterbury Press, 2003.

Questions for discussion
1.   Do you agree that there are degrees of responsibility?
2.   How do you think church members and Christian mental health professionals can guard against judging criminal people who are mentally ill?

Further reading
'Help at Hand' leaflets on common mental health problems. London: Royal College of Psychiatrists, 2002. *www.rcpsych.ac.uk.*

Chapter 5: Treatments used in psychiatry and Christian counselling, by M Dominic Beer

References
1   Rose D, Wykes T, Leese M *et al.* Patients' perspective on electro-convulsive therapy: Systematic review. *BMJ* 2003;326:1363–1365.
2   National Institute of Clinical Excellence (NICE). *Guidance on the Use of Electroconvulsive Therapy.* London: NICE, 2003. *www.nice.org.uk.*
3   Royal College of Psychiatrists. *ECT College Guideline.* London: Royal College of Psychiatrists, 1990.
4   Hurding RF. *Roots and Shoots: A Guide to Counselling and Psychotherapy.* London: Hodder and Stoughton, 2003.
5   Land N. Psychiatry and Christianity. Poles Apart? Part Two. *Nucleus* 2003; April:12–20.
6   Baxter R. *The Signs and Causes of Melancholy.* London: Cruttenden and Cox, 1716.
7   Minirth FB, Byrd W. *Christian Psychiatry.* Grand Rapids: Fleming, H. Revell, 1993.

8   Hurding, 2003 (see ref. 4, p.365).
9   Hurding, 2003 (see ref. 4, p.366).
10   Payne L. *The Healing Presence*. Eastbourne: Kingsway, 1994:115–117.
11   Payne, 1994 (see ref. 10, p.31).
12   Clements R. Demons and the Mind. *Cambridge Papers* 1996;5:3.
13   World Health Organization. *International Classification of Diseases*. Geneva: WHO, 1992.
14   Jamison KR. *An Unquiet Mind. A Memoir of Moods and Madness*. London and Basingstoke: Picador, 1997.
15   Vaughn C, Leff J. The influence of family and social factors on the course of schizophrenic illness. *British Journal of Psychiatry* 1976;129:125–137.
16   Lovell D. *Lives in the Balance. Recovering from Compulsive Eating, Bulimia and Anorexia*. London: Eagle Publishing, 2000.
17   Baker R. *Understanding Panic Attacks and Overcoming Fear*. Oxford: Lion, 1995; Redgrave K. *Anxious Christians. Psychological Problems and the Christian Faith*. London: SPCK, 2000.

Questions for discussion

1.   Would you be prepared to take antidepressant medication if you were depressed, and a GP suggested that you do?

2.   Would you say that interpersonal psychotherapies were compatible with the Christian faith?

3.   How would you help a person with schizophrenia who is in your church home group?

Further Reading

Beer MD. Fit for purpose: is ECT useful or should it be banned? *Triple Helix* 2006 Spring:12–13.

Chave-Jones M. *When the Bough Breaks…Giving your Child Security in an Insecure World*. Leicester: IVP, 1994.

Davies G. *Stress. The Challenge to Christian Caring*. Eastbourne: Kingsway, 1994.

Fowke R. *The Last Straw. Resolving the Build-Up of Stress*. London: Eagle, 2000.

Munro B. *Designer Living. The Way to Beat Stress*. Eastbourne: Monarch, 1991.

White J. *The Masks of Melancholy*. London: IVP, 1985.

Williams C, Richards P, Whitton I. *I'm Not Supposed to Feel Like This. A Christian self-help approach to depression and anxiety*. London: Hodder & Stoughton, 2002.

Chapter 6: Personal responsibility and its relationship to substance misuse, by Christopher C H Cook

References

1   American Psychiatric Association. *Diagnostic and statistical manual of mental disorders (4th edition)*. Washington DC: American Psychiatric Association, 1994.

2   World Health Organisation. *The ICD-10 classification of mental and behavioural disorders*. Geneva: World Health Organisation, 1992.

3   Alcoholics Anonymous. *Alcoholics Anonymous (3rd edition)*. New York: AA World Services Inc, 1976.

4   Alcoholics Anonymous. *Twelve steps and twelve traditions*. New York: Alcoholics Anonymous World Services, 1977.

5   Cook CCH. The Minnesota model in the management of drug and alcohol dependency: miracle method or myth? Part I. The philosophy and the programme. *British Journal of Addiction* 1988a;83:625–634; Cook CCH. The Minnesota model in the management of drug and alcohol dependency: miracle method or myth? Part II. Evidence and conclusions. *British Journal of Addiction* 1988b;83:735–748.

6   Levine HG. The discovery of addiction: Changing conceptions of habitual drunkenness in America. *Journal of Studies on Alcohol* 1978;39:143–174.

7   Pine-Coffin RS (ed). *Saint Augustine: Confessions.* London: Penguin, 1961:173.

8   McFadyen A. *Bound to Sin.* Cambridge: Cambridge University Press, 2000.

9   May GG. *Addiction and Grace.* San Francisco: Harper Collins, 1988.

Questions for study and discussion

1. What is sin?
2. Under what circumstances might people be legally or morally excused for wrong acts?
3. To what extent should the alcoholic be held responsible for their behaviour whilst drinking?
4. To what extent is sin addictive?
5. To what extent is addiction sinful?
6. What can the addictions paradigm teach us about sin?
7. Assuming a common Christian belief that all people require salvation through Christ, how do we see the addict as needing any more, or less, or different, help than any other sinful person?
8. What is the role of specialist services (secular or Christian) for the counselling and treatment of those who are addicted?

Further reading

Edwards G, Marshall EJ, Cook CCH. *The treatment of drinking problems (4th edition).* Cambridge: Cambridge University Press, 2003. An introduction to the causes, nature and treatment of drinking problems for those in the helping professions.

Groves P, Farmer R. Buddhism and addictions. *Addiction Research* 1994;2:183–194. A Buddhist perspective on addiction.

May GG. *Addiction and grace.* San Francisco: Harper Collins, 1988. A useful exploration of the physical, psychological and spiritual aspects of addiction.

Chapter 7: Demons and evil in a Christian context, by Roger C S Moss

References

1   cf Beck JR, Lewis GR. Counselling and the demonic: a reaction to Page. *Journal of Psychology and Theology* 1989;17(2):132–134; Alexander WM. *Demonic Possession in the New Testament.* Edinburgh: T&T Clark, 1902 (quoted by Beck and Lewis); Sims A. Demon possession: medical perspective in a Western Culture. In Palmer B (ed). *Medicine and the Bible.* Exeter: Paternoster Press, 1986:171.

2   1 Jn 3:8, cf Jn 12:31.

3   See for example, theological views in Green M. *I believe in Satan's Downfall.* London: Hodder & Stoughton, 1981; Rose L. *The Devil and the Sovereignty of God.* Eastbourne: Kingsway, 1995: chapter 10 (Demons); and *Report for the House of Bishops. A time to heal.* London: Church House Publishing, 2000:172–175; and psychiatrists who stress its importance, Peck MS. *People of the Lie.(2nd edition).* New York: Touchstone, 1985; Wilson WP. Demon possession and exorcism: a reaction to Page. *Journal of Psychology and Theology* 1989;17(2):135–139.

4   Page SHT. The role of exorcism in clinical practice and pastoral care. *Journal of Psychology and Theology* 1989;17(2):121–131.

5   Wright N. *The fair face of evil.* London: Marshall, Morgan & Scott, 1989, quoted by Walker A. The Devil you think you know: Demonology and the Charismatic Movement. In Smail T, Walker A, Wright N (eds). *Charismatic Renewal.* London: SPCK, 1995: chapter 6.

6   Sims A. Demon possession: medical perspective in a Western Culture. In Palmer B (ed). *Medicine and the Bible.* Exeter: Paternoster Press, 1986:chapter 7:173.

7   Augsburger DW. Possession, shamanism, and healing across cultures. In *Pastoral Counselling across Cultures.* Westminster Press, 1986: chapter 9:33–35.

8   Je 17:9; Mk 7:21–23; Jas 1:14–15.

9   Mt 4:1–11; Acts 5:3; Jn 13:2,27.

10   cf Perry M (ed). *Deliverance: Psychic Disturbances and Occult Involvement.* London: SPCK, 1987.

11   1 Sam 16:14; Lk 13:10–16; 2 Cor 4:4; 1 Tim 4:1.

12   Prins H. Besieged by Devils – thoughts on possession and possession states. *Medicine, Science and the Law* 1992;32(3):237–246.

13   Lk 8:26–39.

14   cf Bourguignon E. The DSM-IV and cultural diversity. *Transcultural Psychiatric Research Review* 1992;29(4):330–332. Quoted by Halperin D. Trance and Possession: are they the same? *Transcultural Psychiatric Research Review* 1996;33:33–41.

15   Oesterreich TK. *Possession: Demoniacal and Other.* New York: New York University, 1966. Quoted by Kemp S, Williams K. Demonic possession and mental disorder in medieval and early modern Europe. *Psychological Medicine* 1987;17:21–29.

16   Report for the House of Bishops. *A time to heal.* London: Church House Publishing, 2000:175.

17   Kemp and Williams, 1987 (see ref.16).

18   eg Enoch MD, Trethowan WH. *Uncommon Psychiatric Syndromes (2nd edition).* Bristol: John Wright & Sons, 1979.

19   Dickason CF. *Demon Possession and the Christian.* Chicago: Moody Press, 1987:40. This begs the question of what such 'residence' means, but it presumably alludes to teaching such as Mt 12:43 where the soul is pictured as a house that an evil spirit can inhabit, leave or return to.

20   Halperin D. Trance and Possession: are they the same? *Transcultural Psychiatric Research Review* 1996;33:33–41.

21   Wilson M. Exorcism: a clinical/pastoral practice which raises serious questions. *The Expository Times* 1975;86:292-295.

22   Bourguignon E. *Religion, Altered States of Consciousness, and Social Change.* Columbus: Ohio State University Press, 1973. Quoted in Gaw AC, Ding QZ, Levine RE, Gaw HF. The clinical characteristics of possession disorder among 20 Chinese patients in the Hebei province of China. *Psychiatric Services* 1998;49(3):360–365.

23   Ross CA, Joshi S. Paranormal experiences in the general population. *Journal of Nervous and Mental Disease* 1992;180:356–360. Quoted in Bull DL, Ellason JW, Ross CA. Exorcism revisited; positive outcomes with dissociative identity disorder. *Journal of Psychology and Theology* 1998;26(2):188–196.

24   Pfeifer S. Demonic attributions in nondelusional disorders. *Psychopathology* 1999;32:252–259.

25   Pfeifer S. Belief in demons and exorcism in psychiatric patients in Switzerland. *British Journal of Medical Psychology* 1994;67(3):247–258.

26   Csordas TJ. The rhetoric of transformation in ritual healing. *Culture, Medicine and Psychiatry* 1983;7:333–375.

27   Trethowan WH. Exorcism: a psychiatric viewpoint. *Journal of Medical Ethics* 1976;2:127–137.

28   Zuk and Zuk have proposed three theories of psychosis – projection, double bind and possession – and describe the possible mechanisms by which these are learnt in early family life. They do not mention dissociation, but perhaps would include it under the category of psychotic behaviour. Zuk GH, Zuk CV. When more is better than less: three theories of psychosis – projection, double bind, and possession. *Contemporary Family Therapy* 1998;20(1):3–13; Zuk GH, Zuk CV. Projection, double bind, and demonic possession: some common elements in three theories of psychosis. *Contemporary Family Therapy* 1998;20(1):15–23.

29   Castillo RJ. Spirit possession in South Asia, dissociation or hysteria? Part 1: Theoretical Background. *Culture, Medicine and Psychiatry* 1994;18:1–21; Castillo RJ. Spirit possession in South Asia, dissociation or hysteria? Part 2: Case Histories. *Culture, Medicine and Psychiatry* 1994;18:141–162.

30   This is apparently not the case in a western country like Switzerland, where only one of Pfeifer's (1994, see ref. 25) sample of 343 showed MPD.

31   Virkler HA, Demonic influence and psychopathology. In Benner DG, Hill PC. *Baker Encyclopedia of Psychology and Counseling*. Grand Rapids: Baker Book House, 1985.

32   Israel M. *Exorcism – the removal of evil influences*. London: SPCK, 1997:79.

33   Kraft C. Demonization and deep-level healing. In *Deep Wounds, Deep Healing*. Lancaster: Sovereign World, 1993:265–267.

34   Perry M (ed). *Deliverance: Psychic disturbances and occult involvement*. London: SPCK 1987: chapter 3.

35   Rosik CK. When discernment fails: the case for outcome studies on Exorcism. *Journal of Psychology and Theology* 1997;25(3):354–363.

36   Whitwell FD, Barker MG. 'Possession' in psychiatric patients in Britain. *British Journal of Medical Psychology* 1980;53:287–295.

37   Koch KE. *Demonology, Past and Present*. Grand Rapids: Kregel Publications, 1973:139. Koch's authoritative work is also worth consulting, namely Koch KE. *Christian Counselling and Occultism: An investigation covering medicine, psychiatry, psychology, depth-psychology, religious psychology, parapsychology, and theology (21st edition)*. Grand Rapids: Kregel, 1973.

38   Koch, 1973 (see ref. 38, p.137).

39   Page SHT. The role of exorcism in clinical practice and pastoral care. *Journal of Psychology and Theology*, 1989;17(2):121–131.

40   White J. Commentary on psychological observations on demonism. In Montgomery JW (ed). *Demon Possession*. Minneapolis: Bethany, 1976:253. Quoted in Page, 1989 (see ref. 39).

41   Sims A. Demon possession: medical perspective in a Western Culture.
     In *Medicine and the Bible*, Palmer B (ed). Exeter: Paternoster Press, 1986:
     chapter 7.

42   Sims, 1986 (see ref. 41, p.126).

43   Sims, 1986 (see ref. 41, p.127).

44   Perry M (ed). *Deliverance: Psychic disturbances and occult involvement.*
     London: SPCK, 1987:77,104.

45   Pfeifer S. Belief in demons and exorcism in psychiatric patients in
     Switzerland. *British Journal of Medical Psychology* 1994;67(3):247–258.

46   Augsburger DW. *Pastoral Counselling across Cultures.* Philadelphia:
     Westminster Press, 1986:302–308.

47   Pfeifer S. Demonic attributions in nondelusional disorders.
     Psychopathology 1999;32:252–259.

48   Whitwell FD, Barker MG. 'Possession' in psychiatric patients in Britain.
     British Journal of Medical Psychology 1980;53:287–295.

49   Augsburger, 1986 (see ref. 46, p.299).

50   Pfeifer S. Demonic attributions in nondelusional disorders.
     Psychopathology 1999;32:252–259.

51   See under 'dissociation' above and further in Castillo RJ. Spirit
     possession in South Asia, Dissociation or Hysteria? Part 1: Theoretical
     Background. *Culture, Medicine and Psychiatry* 1994;18:1–21.

52   Bull DL, Ellason JW, Ross CA. Exorcism revisited; positive outcomes
     with dissociative identity disorder. *Journal of Psychology and Theology*
     1998;26(2):188–196.

53   Lacy TJ, Khatain KG. Obsessive compulsive disorder manifesting as
     demonic attack (letter). *Journal of Clinical Psychiatry* 1993;54(10):398.

54   Ahmed SH. Cultural influences on delusion. *Psychiatria clinica* 1978;11:1–9.

55   Goff DC, Brotman AW, Kindlon D, Waites M, Amico E. The delusion
     of possession in chronically psychotic patients. *Journal of Nervous and
     Mental Disease* 1991;179(9):567–571.

56   American Psychiatric Association. *Diagnostic and statistical manual of
     mental disorders (4th edition).* Washington DC: American Psychiatric
     Association, 1994.

57   Childhood religious abuse seems to be common in many DID patients
     who have previously sought exorcism. Bowman ES. Clinical and
     spiritual effects of exorcism in fifteen patients with Multiple Personality
     Disorder. *Dissociation* 1993;6:222–238; Ross CA, Joshi S. Paranormal
     experiences in the general population. *Journal of Nervous and Mental
     Disease* 1992;180:356–360. Both papers quoted by Rosik, 1997 (see below).

58   Rosik CK. The unification of consciousness: Approaches to the healing
     of dissociation. *Journal of Religion and Health* 1995;34:233–245; Rosik
     CK. When discernment fails: the case for outcome studies on Exorcism.
     Journal of Psychology and Theology 1997;25(3):354–363.

59   Castillo RJ. Spirit possession in South Asia, Dissociation or Hysteria?
     Part 1: Theoretical Background. *Culture, Medicine and Psychiatry*
     1994;18:1–21.

60   Dickason CF. *Demon Possession and the Christian.* Chicago: Moody Press,
     1987:73–213.

61   Kraft C. Demonization and deep-level healing. In *Deep Wounds,
     Deep Healing*. Lancaster: Sovereign World, 1993:259–268.

62   Lawrence P. Healing the Demonised. In Lawrence P. *Doing what comes
     supernaturally.* Bradford on Avon: Terra Nova Publications (Kingsway),
     1992:171–179.

63   Augsburger DW. *Pastoral Counselling across Cultures.* Philadelphia: Westminster Press, 1986 (especially pp. 311–312).

64   Lacy TJ, Khatain KG. Obsessive Compulsive Disorder manifesting as demonic attack (letter). *Journal of Clinical Psychiatry,* 1993;54(10):398.

65   Clements R. Demons and the mind. *Cambridge Papers* 1996,5(3):1–4.

66   Neki JS, Joinet B, Ndosi N, Kilonzo G, Hauli J G, Duvinage G. Witchcraft and psychotherapy: review article. *British Journal of Psychiatry* 1986;149:145–155. This is a wide-ranging and helpful introduction to the subject, though the settings for those working in western countries will be somewhat different.

67   Murphy JK, Brantley PJ. A case study reportedly involving possession. *Journal of Behaviour Therapy & Experimental Psychiatry* 1982;13(4):357–359.

68   Wicker J. Spirit releasement therapy. In Leskowitz ED (ed). *Transpersonal Hypnosis.* London: CRC Press LLC, 2000: chapter 11.

69   Frank JD. Religious and ethical issues in psychotherapy. *Current Opinion in Psychiatry* 1991;4:375–378.

70   Wilson M. Exorcism: A clinical/pastoral practice which raises serious questions. *Expository Times* 1975;86:292–295.

71   Bull DL, Ellason JW, Ross CA. Exorcism revisited; positive outcomes with dissociative identity disorder. *Journal of Psychology and Theology* 1998;26(2):188–196.

72   Pfeifer S. Belief in demons and exorcism in psychiatric patients in Switzerland. *British Journal of Medical Psychology* 1994;67(3):247–258.

73   Rosik CK. When discernment fails: the case for outcome studies on Exorcism. *Journal of Psychology and Theology* 1997;25(3):354–363.

74   Bowman ES. Clinical and spiritual effects of exorcism in fifteen patients with Multiple Personality Disorder. *Dissociation* 1993;6:222–238.

75   Fraser JG. Exorcism rituals: Effects on multiple personality disordered patients. *Dissociation* 1993;6:239–244.

76   Page SHT. The role of exorcism in clinical practice and pastoral care. *Journal of Psychology and Theology* 1989;17(2):121–131.

77   Rosik CK. When discernment fails: the case for outcome studies on Exorcism. *Journal of Psychology and Theology* 1997;25(3):354–363.

78   Allison RB. If in doubt, cast it out? The evolution of a belief system regarding possession and exorcism. *Journal of Psychology and Christianity* 2000;19(2):109–121. Allison is a Californian psychiatrist who relates his own story of moving from rejection of exorcism to using the practice with difficult patients presenting with Multiple Personality Disorder (DID) and the like. His colleagues tried to deny his admitting rights to hospital, and to exercise the power inherent in their use of science as a system of power over the different belief systems of some patients. In the process he offers some interesting insights into psychotherapy with DID patients, and the aspects that can be exorcised by the patient's own 'Inner Self Helper'.

79   cf 1 Cor 9:22,23 and the context of these verses.

80   'Sample differences may account for a great deal of the between group variance in the opinions regarding exorcism among pastors and therapists, where the latter group tends to be more sceptical than the former.' Therapists and pastors are both unlikely to encounter the results of the others' successful practice. Rosik CK. When discernment fails: the case for outcome studies on Exorcism. *Journal of Psychology and Theology* 1997;25(3):354–363; Rosik CK. Establishing a foundation for dialogue: A response to articles on possession, exorcism, and MPD. *Dissociation* 1993;6:245–249; Ross CA. Critical issues committee report: